Helping Young Children with Maths

Sara Williams and Susan Goodman

Hodder & Stoughton

A MEMBER OF THE HODDER HEADLINE GROUP

Orders: please contact Bookpoint Ltd, 78 Milton Park, Abingdon, Oxon OX14 4TD. Telephone: (44) 01235 827720, Fax: (44) 01235 400454. Lines are open from 9.00–6.00, Monday to Saturday, with a 24 hour message answering service. Email address: orders@bookpoint.co.uk

British Library Cataloguing in Publication Data
A catalogue record for this title is available from The British Library

ISBN 0 340 774 568

First published 2000
Impression number   10 9 8 7 6 5 4 3 2 1
Year   2005 2004 2003 2002 2001 2000

Typeset by Fakenham Photosetting Ltd, Fakenham, Norfolk.
Printed in Great Britain for Hodder & Stoughton Educational, a division of Hodder Headline Plc, 338 Euston Road, London NW1 3BH by J.W. Arrowsmith Ltd., Bristol

Contents

Introduction   v

Acknowledgements   vii

Chapter 1   The Beginning of Mathematical Thinking: Babies
             and Toddlers   1

Chapter 2   The Foundations of Maths: Developing Early
             Mathematical Skills   19

Chapter 3   The Foundation of Maths: Developing Pre-school
             Skills   36

Chapter 4   Challenges in Early Maths Education   56

Chapter 5   Beginning Maths at School   78

Chapter 6   Using Maths Across the Curriculum   97

Chapter 7   Developing Maths and Support Outside School   109

Chapter 8   Moving on with Maths   122

Glossary   132

Appendix 1   Some ideas for books to use with children   135
             Useful Resources for Adults   137

Appendix 2   Baseline Assessment   140
             The National Numeracy Strategy   140
             Early Learning Goals   141

Appendix 3   Other Resources   142

Index   149

Introduction

Mathematics is part of the language of our everyday lives. We use it to shop, cook, budget our finances or read a bus timetable. Mathematical words and ideas are woven into our conversations. It may not seem like maths because it is not happening at a desk in a classroom. However it is the same maths that we learnt at school, now applied to the wider world. The experience of mathematical learning is much bigger than that of the classroom.

Babies are born into this mathematical world, and in this book we look at how maths is incorporated naturally into babies' lives, how toddlers and young children 'play' maths and how children start to explore more formal ideas in maths at school and at home. We revisit many key ideas in many different ways as children get older and their interests and abilities change.

Although much of this book is focused on helping students on CACHE and BTEC early years courses, we are aware that it will also be of direct relevance to classroom teachers, assistants and parents. This book is designed to provide a rich source of practical ideas and useful information to help develop maths skills in young children. Details for all books and resources mentioned in the text are listed at the back of the book.

We realise that very few people will specialise in maths teaching, but it is important that everyone working and caring for young children recognises how easy and enjoyable it can be to support their mathematical learning.

Acknowledgements

Sara Williams and Susan Goodman would like to thank everyone who has helped us with the research, writing and illustrations for this book.

Our children Steven and Callum Williams and Benjamin, Daniel and Anton Goodman as well as other members of our families, especially Deborah Williams, Graham Davies, Kate Williams, Nina Williams and David Goodman, have contributed in many wonderful ways. Thank you.

Our thanks also go to the children, parents and staff of Elms Road Nursery School, Oxford and North Hinksey CE Primary School, Oxford. Particular help has been given by Carol Camping, Joy Taylor, Duncan Spence, Ann Taylor, Wendy Plested, Alex Reed and John Sloboda. Simon Taylor contributed some lovely photographs. There are many other adults and children who have made valuable contributions to this book in a variety of ways. We greatly appreciate all your help.

Last but not least, thank you to all our pupils for all they have taught us.

1

The Beginning of Mathematical Thinking: Babies and Toddlers

The ideas and language of maths are all around us. They are a central part of how we interpret our world and we learn about them from our earliest days onwards. Whether or not we think of ourselves as being 'good at maths' is not the issue. We all communicate using mathematical words and concepts everyday without being aware of them; they are a natural part of our experience and our understanding of the world we live in.

We can provide children with all sorts of rich experiences that will help them to enjoy and understand their world more fully, and this includes the mathematical ideas in it. Once again, for most of us, this is natural and we do it instinctively. It is part of our caring for the children we look after professionally and as parents. Enjoyment of the world around them and the process of learning can be the same thing.

In this chapter we look at examples of the mathematical experience of babies and toddlers from birth to about two years of age. The developmental sequence we use of 'the new born baby', 'the settled baby', 'sitting-up', 'beginning mobility' and 'walking' is that followed by the majority of young children. However, we appreciate that there may be differences and ask you to be flexible in your interpretation of our ideas if they do not fit completely with your experience of the children in your care. For example, some babies spend very little time sitting before they get on the move and babies with physical disabilities may follow quite a different pattern of mobility. All babies follow slightly different patterns anyway and generalisations, such as those we have made here, need to be seen in that light.

Very first experiences

From the moment babies enter the world they are bombarded with sounds, smells, images and sensations. The brain immediately begins the enormous task of sorting out this jumble of messages from all the senses. It is probably more confusing than we could possibly imagine.

Our first intuitive response is to hold tiny babies quietly, gently, lovingly. We use rhythm to rock them to sleep. We murmur words and songs to reassure and comfort them. We may stroke them or gently pat them. Babies show an immediate response to rhythmic patterns. This is hardly surprising when you think about a baby in the womb surrounded by the regular thumping of their mother's heartbeat. When she went for a walk the baby would be rocked and bounced, cushioned by the surrounding amniotic fluid.

A baby is born with an established awareness of rhythm. In the context of this book, this is important because rhythm is a simple pattern or sequence. Many mathematical ideas use patterns and sequences. Counting is a good example of this. A young child's inbuilt sense of rhythm will be part of the foundations for their understanding of these kinds of concepts when they are older.

Talking together

At our first meeting with a baby most of us will begin to talk to it. We don't stop to think about the meaninglessness of our chatter. Intuitively, we take on the role of teaching this baby to speak. We help the child to learn about taking turns in communication. They make a noise or change their facial expression. We copy them. They 'say' something. We reply as if we understand their 'words'. The act of conversation, of taking turns, is a predictable sequence of events. Sequences, even simple ones of the 'you-me-you-me' type, are found in maths.

The type of speech we use (which has been named 'motherese', 'parentese' or 'infant directed speech') is rhythmic, repetitive and not too fast. We sound affectionate and loving. We talk face to face with good eye contact. We may reinforce our language with movements that match it. Early communication is packed full of sequences and patterns and, in addition, scattered among all our words will be some that have mathematical meanings: 'What a *big* smile!', '*Up* you come!', 'Let's put you *on* the changing mat'. The words in italics all have mathematical content. They are about size and position.

We use mathematical words and concepts throughout our everyday lives without noticing. It can be surprising to realise how much of our language links to maths and that we are already experts in its use.

A C T I V I T Y

When you next hold a baby, share the pleasure of rhythm with them by singing songs and rhymes. Sing anything you enjoy – something from the current charts, an operatic aria, an advert from the television, or just something you've made up. If the baby enjoys more physical movement, you can bounce them in time to the music and dance together. Dancing can calm down stressful moments for everyone. One father we know found that his baby son especially enjoyed dancing to his collection of reggae music. There are many cassettes and CDs of songs for young children that you can also use.

A C T I V I T Y

Songs and rhymes can have 'mathematical value' in the words they use as well. Traditional baby rhymes such as *Round and round the garden, like a teddy bear, one step, two steps* . . . introduce counting and sequences of physical actions. *This little piggy went to market, this little piggy stayed at home* . . . uses the same sort of verbal sequence, reinforced with physical play. Take a closer look at some of the words and sequences in your favourite traditional rhymes for babies. Is there a mathematical basis to any of them? For example, are any of the words connected to shape, size, position or number?

Awareness of shape and space

Even very young babies seem to be pre-programmed to recognise the simple pattern made by the features of a human face. You have to get quite close for the baby to be able to focus on your eyes and mouth and so identify 'a face' but, as the weeks pass, the baby will develop the ability to focus and see things further away. They will begin to understand the three-dimensional nature of the world around them.

Of course the development of three-dimensional vision and spatial awareness is a basic necessity, fundamental to our need to move around in our environment. These same spatial skills are also part of many mathematical activities where understanding of shape is required. Moreover, children who have a good understanding of the three-dimensional world in which they live can easily interpret the two-dimensional world they see in pictures.

Mobiles are toys designed to engage babies' attention and they help to stimulate spatial awareness. The objects on them move in relation to each other and so are seen in lots of different positions. Bright, bold pictures on the wall also catch the eye, but moving objects such as mobiles seem to be more attractive to babies. Plenty of parents and carers have discovered that parking a baby's pram near the branch of a tree as it waves in the breeze, or the washing blowing about on the line, will keep the child occupied for a long time. Likewise some young babies are enthralled by watching a front-loading washing machine in action (especially if the clothes are in clearly contrasting colours). Young babies making sense of the shapes and spatial relationships in the world about them spend a lot of time looking at moving objects. They return to movement again and again.

ACTIVITY

If you are the carer of a young baby, spend time watching what they watch. What are the things they like to look at? Do they prefer moving objects to still ones? Watch them looking at trees on a breezy day, a flock of pigeons in the park, seagulls at the beach and so on.

Summary

- We live in a world where mathematical language and ideas are woven through our everyday lives.
- Babies are very responsive to sequences of events and rhythmic patterns in sound, speech and movement.
- Babies show preferences for certain spatial arrangements of shapes, such as human faces, and seem to enjoy focusing on moving, three-dimensional arrangements.
- The ability to recognise sequences, patterns and spatial relationships is important for later mathematical learning.

The settled baby

After a few months many babies will become more settled; their bodies and senses will have adjusted to the world. They start to recognise familiar faces and respond with big smiles. It can feel easier to hold 'conversations' and often these are a baby's favourite activities.

Of course many of these early conversations with babies relate to their physical care, for example changing a nappy, dressing, feeding or bathing.

Invariably most of this talking is done privately when carer and baby are alone together. This privacy is invaluable as it makes the carer less self-conscious and enables focused concentration on the baby. The result is that ordinary routine activities are transformed into rich learning opportunities.

Many parents and carers will give a baby a detailed description of the procedure they are carrying out, for example when nappy changing. The baby does not remain passive throughout the 'conversation': gurgles, smiles, kicking and waving will keep them as an active partner. Most of these caring activities are repeated several times every day and so the same phrases, words and actions are experienced many times over by the child. Much of the language already being used will have mathematical relevance and it is easy to develop it a little further if you want.

Bath time

Bath time is another opportunity for lots of physical interaction. The series of events surrounding bath time – the sound of running water, the changing out of clothes, the playing and splashing in the bath itself, the cuddles and drying, then being dressed – is one of the most predictable patterns of sequences of activity in most small children's daily lives.

Dressing

Here is part of a carer's monologue when dressing a young baby:

> 'Where's your vest? Here it is *on* the table. This *one* is too *small* for you now. You need a *bigger one*. Let's put your arms *through* here. Here's *one* arm and here's *the other*. Here are your socks. *One* for this foot . . . and *one* for this foot'.

This is the sort of conversation any of us might have without noticing it. It couldn't be simpler and yet it contains references to: size (*small, bigger*); the concepts of pairs (*one* and *the other*); correspondence of numbers (matching a number, *one*, with an object, *sock*); and positional words (*on, through*). The baby will not understand any of the words yet but they will be starting to hear the same sounds repeatedly used in varying ways. It is about sharing the language we use to communicate.

It is also very common for counting to be introduced while dressing a baby. You can count buttons and toggles, fingers and toes, even when the baby is too young to be aware of what you are doing. If you enjoy filling your conversations with counting then we encourage you to continue. The counting sequence is one that all children will eventually encounter and learn. It does not matter how young they are when they begin to hear it. Counting is, after all, a part of our everyday language.

Hands-on exploration

As babies start to explore their physical environment, they will be learning more about space and shapes. When they are only a few months old, they will begin to want to reach out to objects.

ACTIVITY

A baby needs to be given lots of opportunities to practise reaching out towards, and making contact with, an object in order to understand exactly where it is. You can give babies this experience even before they can purposefully grab anything. A small toy, which makes a sound when hit, can be hung within striking distance of a baby. A suitable rattle, or toy with a bell, can be suspended from a piece of elastic strung across a cot or pram. **(Do remember to stay aware of safety though.)** Commercially made 'baby gyms', with frameworks on which to hang toys, are designed for this stage in development. If you are looking to buy this kind of toy we recommend you get one where the objects to be suspended can be changed around and different toys and rattles can be added – babies like variety.

Once a baby can reach out, grab and hold an object, this becomes a favourite activity. The baby must now learn to estimate the distance to the object. In other words, is it within grabbing distance? Once objects can be held they are quickly brought to the mouth. It is as if the mouth forms the central reference point, as well as helping to explore the nature of the object. The mouth is the centre of the baby's three-dimensional world. The mathematical idea of measurement starts with a baby becoming familiar with distance in relation to itself.

At this stage of development, babies who are carried and included in everyday activities will find plenty in their environment to explore, especially the hair, jewellery and clothing of the people who look after them. They need to be allowed to explore safely in this way. They are engaged in important learning about shape and space.

Summary

- We use mathematical language naturally, as part of our normal speech.
- Repetitive conversations with familiar words and phrases, linked to the practical everyday activities of caring for a baby such as bath time or dressing, can be full of mathematical language.
- Learning to reach out, touch, grab and manipulate objects and put them in the mouth, is mathematically important for babies because they are learning about shape, space, distance and measurement in relation to their own bodies.

The 'sitting-up' baby

Once babies can sit up alone they are better placed to reach for things in their immediate environment. They can twist round to see a wider view of the surrounding world. Their mental picture of how objects are placed in that world becomes more sophisticated. A baby who is seated can more easily be included in conversations in a group, including those at meal times.

Conversations

A baby's awareness of turn-taking in speech develops from the simplicity of the earliest 'conversations' to more elaborate patterns, sequences and rules. At about nine months babies may follow conversations between other people, turning their heads to see who is speaking, watching a sequence taking place away from themselves.

As a baby's comprehension increases you might want consciously to talk about events in the environment relating to space. 'Look at the plane *up* there in the sky', 'Can you see the squirrel hiding *behind* that tree?' Emphasise what you say with gestures and pointing.

Physical play

A great deal of shared fun with a baby of any age involves physical activities. The process for a baby of learning to sit and balance inevitably involves much sitting *up* and falling *down*.

By the middle of the first year, a baby may really enjoy the sheer pleasure of romping and rolling around. Some babies seem to enjoy this rough and

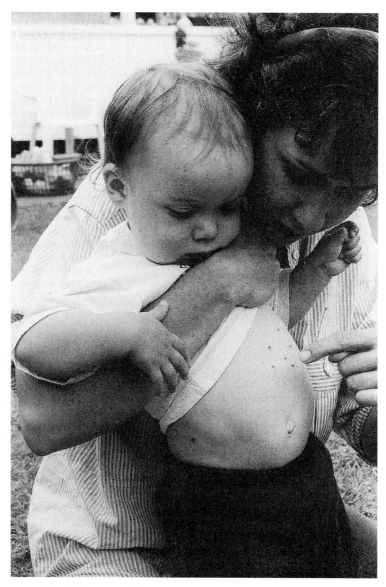

You can count anything: 'How many chickenpox spots have you got today?'.

tumble more than others, so sensitivity to the personality and preferences of the baby is paramount. Generally much of this physical play can involve counting to increase the anticipation of the next event. For example '*one, two, three*' can be said to precede a bounce, swing or roll. You can count the swings and bounces, using words such as '*bigger*' and '*higher*' as the play becomes more vigorous. You could use '*biggest*' or '*highest*' at the final, most stupendous event. Playing 'boo' games, bouncing around in baby swimming lessons or gently swinging on the baby swing in the park are ideal opportunities for using the idea of counting. If you feel comfortable about counting and you get into the habit of doing it you will find that it really does become second nature to you in all sorts of play with babies.

One parent we know had to manage four flights of stairs to her flat and she used to count them aloud every time she went up or down them. Initially she used it as a means of encouraging herself while carrying her baby and the shopping, but it became a game when she could see her daughter expecting to hear these words. As the child got older she began to join in. Her idea of counting was much greater than the limited 'one to five' or 'one to ten' we expect of young children. Linking the physical bounce the child felt in her body with a number word as they counted up to 48 each time they went upstairs must have helped her equate a separate word with a separate thing (in this case, a bounce). This is a crucial part of understanding how numbers work and, as in this case, it can begin at a very young age, quite naturally for baby and carer, as part of ordinary daily activities.

A C T I V I T Y

Try to identify where you use counting words with a young baby in your care. Even if you shy away from maths, we are sure you will find some activities where you naturally use numbers.

Water play

When a baby is able to sit independently in a bath, bath toys can be enjoyed. We can describe all sorts of events that happen in play with mathematical words. A toy duck floats *away* from you or *towards* you. We hold things *above* or *below* the water. A yoghurt pot is *full* of water or *empty*. The dry sponge is *light*, while the saturated one is *heavy*.

Older babies and toddlers can start to discover that if you do something first (such as overloading a toy boat) another thing follows (the boat sinks): cause and effect. Along with this, the child begins to learn that things sometimes have to be done in a particular order – the sunken boat must be emptied before it can float again, then the loading–sinking sequence can be repeated. That sense of doing things step by step, in a simple logical sequence, can begin at a young age in a simple, experimental way. It is yet another small preparation for developing the skills required for mathematical thought.

Toddlers sinking and floating 'boats'.

The urge to copy you

In the second half of their first year, as babies are able to do more and more things with their hands, you will find that they want to copy your actions. Their manual and spatial skills increase as they watch and try to copy activities in the world around them. Have a go at demonstrating how to push a toy car, pour water out of a beaker in the bath, put a teddy in a basket, hit a tin can with a metal spoon. If it is a new activity, the baby will probably want to copy you straight away. Supporting their development of spatial skills will help with their later mathematical learning about shape and space.

Nursery rhymes

There is a real value in traditional nursery rhymes. This is not in the (often rather meaningless) stories they tell, but in their powerful, repetitive rhythms, tunes and word patterns. Many rhymes also have counting as part of their structure. Rhythm, pattern and counting are all part of early maths, and traditional nursery rhymes provide good foundations.

There are many music groups around the country for babies and toddlers and their parents and carers. The adults present usually do most of the 'work' but after some time even the youngest children become able to anticipate their favourites, especially action songs. Apart from the fun, social value and the benefits from hearing music and rhymes, going to this sort of group can also be a way to get access to musical instruments that would not usually be available in the home: a toddler-strength, large glockenspiel or a drum that can be hit by several toddlers at once, for example. Percussion instruments enhance the learning of spatial skills by rewarding actions with wonderful noises – cause and effect again.

Feeding

Once a baby is eating off a spoon, there are many words we use that have a mathematical meaning: counting mouthfuls, words to do with quantity or concepts such as 'full' or 'empty'. The words 'first', 'second' and 'third' (called **ordinal numbers** in maths) can also be used when counting spoonfuls. The fact of eating something 'first' or 'before' another item of food is often referred to. In some families dessert or pudding is called 'seconds' or 'afters'. Reluctant eaters are coaxed with 'one, two, three and in it goes'. Constantly, number order is being established and reinforced.

Manipulating food is wonderful for the development of spatial awareness. A baby who picks up a piece of apple and gets it into their mouth, drops it and repeats the process, will be using lots of hand-eye co-ordination and estimation of distances. A child in a high chair who is at the developmental stage where they need to drop toys and food onto the floor, or throw food at the walls, will be engaged in activities that are a rich source of mathematical words. Food is dropped *down* onto the floor. It drips *down* the walls. Toys are picked *up* and put back *on* the high chair tray. Items that roll are not only dropped *down*, they also roll *under* the furniture. The sequence of dropping and retrieval is exciting for the baby, has a clear mathematical content and is often extremely exasperating for the carer!

Using books

It is never too soon to introduce a baby to books. Many parents and carers start using books with babies once they reach the sitting-up stage and libraries will happily enrol baby members this young. It is well worth investing in some of the many robust board books available; there are now many high-quality books for this age group.

A mathematical content can be identified or created when reading most picture books with children. Of course, like the natural use of mathematical words in our everyday speech, the use of mathematical language when sharing books with babies will happen automatically without us noticing it.

We may explore the mathematical content of books by:

- starting at the *front* of the book, on the *first* page, or finding a page in the *middle* to talk about
- counting similar items on a page, for example the babies in Janet and Allan Ahlberg's *The Baby's Catalogue*
- looking for pictures *under* the flaps in a 'lift-the-flap' book
- finding objects or characters that are *up, down, in, on, under, behind, in front* and so on, and naming the positions that these things take in the illustration
- finding *one* thing then looking for the *other* like it, where there are two things the same
- finding groups of similar objects – e.g. all the ducks in the pond or all the frogs – and naming each group
- using pictures to compare sizes, e.g. *big* and *small* (books with adult and baby animals automatically lend themselves to this)
- reading books with very strong sequences of events, such as *Dressing* by Helen Oxenbury or *Rosie's Walk* by Pat Hutchins
- remembering sequences in familiar books. Very often books with animals and animal noises are popular for this. A baby who is not talking might remember that the page after the picture of the 'moo' is 'miaow' and the page after that will be the cue for a gigantic and dramatic growl. Sequences of noises are still sequences.

ACTIVITY

Take a look at one of your favourite baby books. What mathematical language can you find in it and what could you introduce in sharing it with a young child?

Summary

- A baby who is able to sit up unaided has wider access to their environment, being able to turn, reach things and join in conversations more easily.
- They will be able to improve their co-ordination and spatial skills through independent exploration of the objects they can now reach.
- If you choose, you can find many opportunities to incorporate counting into your play with babies.
- When we talk with babies as they play we instinctively use simple

mathematical language including words linked to position, cause and effect, shape and space, quantity, size and sequences as well as number words.

- Reading picture books with babies is another way to extend their vocabulary, including their mathematical vocabulary, while having fun.

Beginning mobility

The concept of space and distance between a baby and the objects around them reaches a new level once they become mobile. Measurement becomes very sophisticated. Newly mobile babies suddenly have a massive increase in things to explore, and their concept of distance is now linked to the speed at which they can travel to the object they are aiming for. Determined, mobile babies may move very fast. Toys that roll or can be pushed or pulled start to be fascinating.

Words such as *fast* and *slow* may begin to have some meaning now. Likewise *up* and *down* take on more significance when crawling begins to turn into stair-climbing.

Exploration of the kitchen

Babies who are on the move exploring their environment will begin to delight in taking things out of boxes, cupboards, baskets, bags and drawers. Low cupboards in the kitchen, full of safe things to play with, are a treat (remember to secure any unsafe cupboards or to transfer their contents well out of reach). All the usual mathematical vocabulary can be used and, if cupboards contain shelves, this may give you the chance to talk about *top*, *middle* or *bottom* shelves too. The child will not understand fully many of the other concepts you use, but by talking you are laying foundations for future understanding.

Most babies start with the need to empty things first. Emptying child-safe bags of shopping is great fun. Tidying things away, putting things back into containers, baskets and cupboards – the opposite to the emptying out phase – seems to become interesting later on. When this point comes you can help by giving them lots of different sized boxes for putting things in. A clean egg box with a lid can be a lovely toy at this stage, if the child is not keen on eating it. Putting a safe toy in each section and taking them out again can be an activity that will keep a child's attention for a long time. Mathematically, the child is linking one object with one space to put it in. The correspondence of a number to an object is fundamental to our understanding of numbers. You may want to count the objects in and count them out repeatedly with the child if they enjoy hearing the words but, even if it is wordless, their playing involving the concept of correspondence is very important.

Food in containers is fascinating. Tins and other cylindrical containers are exciting: they come in different sizes, can be used to build towers and can be rolled across the floor or down slopes. Long cardboard packing tubes roll well and, if they have a large enough diameter, can have things rolled through them too, which is surprising for the child.

Putting things away logically in groups is something that a very young child can start to help with. They can put all the apples into the fruit bowl or the potatoes in the vegetable rack. Grouping things according to certain attributes is an idea used in maths to the highest level.

Posting things

As a baby develops, the idea of putting things *in* and *out* of containers turns into 'posting' and this soon becomes a firm favourite. Babies seem to want to test which object can fit into which gap or hole. This is the phase that generates reports of credit cards being posted through gaps in floorboards or items of food disappearing, only to be found later in the gap between cushions on the sofa. Despite the mathematical benefit to be derived from these activities, you will reach a limit to what is acceptable: discovering that peanut butter sandwiches fit exactly into the slot in the video machine (not unknown) might be one mathematical activity to discourage!

ACTIVITY

Shop-bought posting toys are often too complicated for beginners at posting. Try cutting a couple of circular holes in the lid of a shoe box and give your baby a collection of cotton reel spools to post through them. Circular holes seem to be an easy shape to start with.

When the child is ready for more, extend the number of different shaped holes and provide more objects for posting into them. Supermarket reward cards fit into slots, bricks fit into rectangular holes and so on. You can have interesting discussions about what *fits*, what is *too big* or *too small*. Turn things around and try again. Perhaps the object is '*too wide* this way' or '*too long*'. In this way, the child's vocabulary grows and so does their understanding of size. Fitting smaller objects into small spaces helps the child with their fine motor skills as well.

Shop-bought toys

Often everyday objects that were never designed to be toys seem to have more play value than shop-bought toys. However, some bought toys seem to be timeless and offer much play potential.

Little buckets – the sort that can be used in the sandpit or in the bath and can be easily carried – are very useful as containers to put things in. A small basket serves a similar purpose when the child reaches the 'putting things in' phase.

There are many shape-fitting toys on the market for children in this age-group. These include posting boxes mentioned previously and simple wooden boards in which to insert large pegs. In this category of toy are also simple tray puzzles, some of which have knobs on the pieces to make it easier for small hands to lift them in and out.

A large set of wooden blocks will be used for many years. Toddlers will build towers, houses or enclosures for toy animals. A set of stacking beakers may also have a lot of play value.

A few toy balls of a size that can be easily picked up provide a useful contrast to bricks. Learning that if you put a cubic brick down on a smooth floor it stays put, but if you put a ball down on that surface it may roll in any direction away from you, is a mathematical lesson. Cylinders – cylindrical bricks or tins from the kitchen – behave in a different way again.

Very often a child will discover these ideas from independent play, but sometimes if they appear to be tiring of their toys you can find something new to show them which will generate a new interest. Demonstrating a spatial skill at just the right time may be enormously helpful. 'Can you roll a ball into a bucket on its side?' 'If you turn the jigsaw piece a little will it fit in the tray?' 'Can you put a long brick across two narrow ones to make a tunnel for a toy car?' Talking about what is happening as you join in with the child's play, or demonstrate a new idea, will provide good opportunities for using mathematical language and for helping them to think about new ideas.

First words and food

Perhaps the most common word used during feeding is *more*. We insist on offering *more* or asking if a baby wants *more*. It is hardly surprising that this becomes one of the first words that babies say. Cause and effect is very clear: if you want more food, say 'more' and then you will get it. Mathematically speaking, 'more' is linked to an increase in quantity or addition.

Young children are often handed two biscuits or two pieces of fruit, 'one for this hand ... and one for the other'. They quickly learn that when there is one in each hand they have their full quota. Of course, eating one handful immediately frees their hand to receive another: 'There's only one left'. When the hand is refilled: 'How many are there now?'. Counting to *two* makes sense in terms of eating what is in your hands. Subtracting by

Learning to share toys: one each.

eating also makes sense. Of course, young children will not encounter this in an abstract written way until they are much older. However, the process of understanding 'one', 'two', 'a pair', 'the other', 'adding' and 'taking away' can actually begin very young, even before children are two years old and are speaking much themselves.

Summary

- Mobile babies are able, independently, to extend their concept of distance and speed.
- Activities relating to removing and replacing objects, putting them in containers and posting them, have a strong mathematical content and develop ideas of size, shape and fitting, space and position. They also develop fine motor skills.
- Using shapes for building and for rolling helps with the understanding of the properties of solids.
- Demonstrating spatial skills, presenting new ideas for play and talking about them can extend a child's ideas and vocabulary.
- Children can begin to make sense of simple, practical mathematical ideas involving one or two objects, especially food, at a very early age.

Confident walking

Once a child is walking confidently their favourite possession may well be their shoes or wellington boots. Pairs become a central part of the business of walking and nursery rhymes such as *Diddle, diddle, dumpling, my son John* reflect the 'one shoe off, one shoe on' language with which everyone is familiar in the conversations that take place when dressing a child.

Once walking, children start to go *up* and *down* steps and slopes themselves. They go *on* and *under*, *in* and *out*, or climb *on* and *off*. Words to do with space and position take on a different meaning – the child can begin to internalise the meanings of these words if you chat with them about it while you share their activities.

Using early language

Some children will have no speech by the time they are two years old, some will be very fluent speakers and most will be somewhere in between, determinedly experimenting with speech and rapidly increasing the vocabulary they are willing to use. They will be trying out many of the words they have heard spoken to them again and again – and using them rather than understanding them is not always straightforward.

Babies' simple classification of objects into groups moves from their being able to sort things in a physical way, to their finding the abstract verbal description of the grouping. One child we know referred to the family cat, Pepper, as 'Beh-puh', but this was also the term she used for all animals of a four-legged nature. Gradually her classification of 'Beh-puhs' moved into using 'horse' and 'pig' and other animals' names, and only cats were called 'Beh-puh'. Later still she realised that 'Beh-puh' was part of a group called cats and the name everyone called this cat at home was special to it alone. For lots of children, the process of classification is similar for animals, objects and people. At first it seems as if their use of language lags behind their thought processes but the two seem to align very quickly.

Similarly, it takes some time for the use of positional words to make sense. Young children often use the words 'up' and 'down' indiscriminately to mean 'move-me-from-the-place-I-am-currently-in'. It can help to reinforce their understanding by using the words regularly in your conversations with them if this confusion arises. They will sort out the difference if you name lots of examples of *up* and *down* as they happen.

The developing richness of children's spoken language will continue apace through the next phase of their development and we look at this further in Chapter 2.

Summary

- Mobile children can understand words connected to position and space by relating them to their own bodies as they move around.
- Early vocabulary includes sorting out the abstract use of words for groups of people or things and the exact use of positional words.
- Mathematical learning starts at birth and is part of our learning about the world we live in and our ability to describe the things we find around us.

2

The Foundations of Maths: Developing Early Mathematical Skills

Children's all-round abilities continue to develop and grow in many exciting ways over the next few years. Their increasing co-ordination, mastery of spoken language, social skills and enthusiasm in practising the activities they see used in their world provide many easy ways for us to support their understanding of some of the foundations for maths.

The rate of children's learning varies greatly from two to three years old – the examples we use in this chapter might be relevant to one child who has just had their second birthday, or another who is three and a half. Do stay aware of the spectrum of ability and learning.

Although many children of this age will be being cared for in day-care settings, much care is still home-based with parents, nannies or childminders. This chapter concentrates more on home-based learning but its ideas are easily adaptable for group-care settings. Chapter 3 will focus more on older, pre-school children at playgroups and nurseries.

Developing physical skills

Frustration and achievement

The increase in a child's physical abilities continues once it has mastered walking; the determination to acquire physical skills can be phenomenal. A two-year-old may want to dress, feed and wash themselves, help you with everything, run faster, balance on high walls, climb out of reach or try equipment designed for older children. At two and three years of age, children seem to become more aware of their own body size, identifying and pushing their limits. They judge many things against themselves: the wall is too high to climb; the bucket of stones is too heavy to carry. The frustration they may experience in wanting to master these activities, but being unable to do so just yet, can be equally phenomenal.

'Aren't you high up!'

Sharing the language used to describe what they want, and can already achieve, sometimes helps to overcome feelings of frustration. It is easier to take clothes *off* than put them *on* so encouraging the independent removal of garments – at appropriate times – makes sense. Some clothes are easier to put on than others: hats and wellington boots are fairly easy; coats, if baggy enough, may come next. Celebrating little achievements – 'Look you've put *one* arm *through* the sleeve!' – helps to acknowledge progress and provides the child with the language to describe the action. Many parents and carers comment that children who are early talkers have fewer problems with frustration (the so-called 'terrible twos') than those who are later at getting started with using language.

Mobility means more mathematical ideas

When a child walks on a wall holding your hand you can talk about their height in relation to you: 'Aren't you *high up!* You're *higher than the buggy.*' Maybe even: 'You're *higher than me!*' Likewise, if you reach the *end* of the wall, say so. If you jump them *down* at the end, say so. The words describe useful concepts in space and position.

Young, mobile children discover through experience that walking up a hill gets to be tiring work and becomes slower the more tired you get. Running down a hill is easy, fast and very exciting. They may begin to understand the words relating to speed in relation to their own bodies, especially being pushed fast in the pushchair. The speed of the snail on the path, or the dog chasing after a stick, will also take on new meanings. It can be fun to try to walk *as slowly as a snail* and run *as fast as the squirrel* climbing up the tree.

From the moment a child is mobile, the pull to move further away from the primary carer increases. Small children are forever moving away and returning. Distance becomes measured in relation to the adult–child gap. Running away becomes a good game when the child is confident enough and you can start to use terms such as *'a long way away'* or *'come closer'*. Distance, speed, acceleration and deceleration, are mathematical concepts.

ACTIVITY

Next time you are out-of-doors with an active two-year-old, listen to the mathematical language you use as you play. See how many mathematical words you use in one visit to the park or playground – you will be surprised.

Discovering new toys

Children may get extremely frustrated at not being able to get toys to work, especially toys that involve fitting and assembling activities. It can become very important to provide toys that they can cope with on a day-to-day basis. You can then introduce more challenging activities in a gentle way. New jigsaws are a good example.

Consider the following. A two-year-old child may help to carry a new tray jigsaw, then decide to tip all the pieces on the floor. You help by starting to turn the pieces over so that the pictures show. The child copies. All the time you talk about what is happening. You twist all the pictures around so that they are upright in relation to the child. They see the one with a car on it and name it. You pick it up and put it in the car-shaped gap in the tray for them. They take it out and drop it. You do it again. They pick it up then try to fit it back. You give them time to try on their own. They start to sound frustrated so you gently help them to nudge the piece in. You wait. The child picks up the teddy picture. You talk about finding a space that will fit the teddy. The child, independently, tries several wrong spaces and you say: 'Does it fit? . . . No? . . . Try another one . . .', until, quite by accident, the right gap is found and minimal help is needed from you to get the piece to fit.

This helping, watching and responding is done in such a way that the child is encouraged to learn by tiny increments. You are providing a structure for them which enables them to climb a fraction higher on the ladder of their learning. That is why this method of enabling learning to take place has been called 'scaffolding'. It can be a very effective way to support young children who are eager to learn new spatial skills that are physically within their capabilities, but whose level of frustration − if left to their own devices − is high.

Playing alongside children in a structured way with newly encountered construction or shape-fitting toys can bring those toys within the child's abilities very quickly. A few days later the child with the jigsaw may be able to assemble it all on their own with no support from you and their level of enjoyment and satisfaction will be high. Manipulating objects in two- and three-dimensions is helpful for the understanding of more advanced maths involving shape and space. Being able to see an object and mentally twist it round to see whether it fits is an ability frequently used in later study of shape, including geometry.

ACTIVITY

If you are working with a child who is enjoying playing with simple jigsaws or construction toys, reserve or borrow one they haven't seen before in order to share it with them. When you do give it to them, stay and watch carefully so that you are able to support their learning in little stages. Take your cues from them and, giving them the space to experiment themselves, offer ideas for 'the next little step' if they need it. Watch the child playing with the same toy over the course of the next week or so. Can you see the way they take this first learning and master the skills needed to enjoy playing with the toy?

The maths of children's own bodies

Once a child can stand, some families and carers begin to keep a note of the child's growth using marks on a door frame or a measuring chart stuck to the wall. Young children begin to understand that the marks are getting higher and that it has something to do with them growing taller. Likewise, some families keep hand or footprints of their children as they grow. Seeing a baby's hand print, followed by others at yearly intervals, is a lovely way to compare sizes. Talking about your adult hand in comparison with the child's, and theirs in comparison with a younger sibling's, helps to make sense of **comparative sizes**: small, smaller, smallest. Using story books, or non-fiction, with good pictures illustrating comparative size can be helpful too. The most obvious of these stories is *Goldilocks and the Three Bears*, which can easily be told without a book using hands to indicate dimensions: the daddy bear is enormous with a big, deep voice, a bowl as big as your arms, and so on. You can act out the story with props using three differently sized teddies, bowls, seats and beds and that works very well too.

Cutting nails can be made more fun if you count the finger and toe nails as they are cut. An awareness of the very useful calculator we have on our hands (the fingers) can start very young. An understanding of the concept of 'ten' (the number system we most often work with) is crucial for numeracy and we both believe very strongly in the benefits of using fingers for counting. Nail-cutting is an easy place to begin.

Summary

- The increase in a child's physical abilities means that they can start to explore ideas to do with distance, speed, height and weight more easily.

- Structured support in learning about new toys, especially puzzles and construction toys, can help two- to three-year-olds acquire new spatial skills with minimal frustration.
- Measuring a child and comparing them with younger babies or physically larger people can enable the use of words connected with comparative sizes.
- Recognising the fact that the fingers on your own hands can be linked to counting will prove very useful later on.

Increased use of language

Classifying and grouping

At the end of Chapter 1 we mentioned children's first attempts to find words to group and classify objects. As a child's mental concepts develop, the language they use reflects that more sophisticated understanding. A general term (e.g. 'cat' for all animals) slowly gets subdivided into many words to describe different animals.

Looking at similarities and differences between objects can help children to become aware of the ways in which we may choose to group things. Collecting leaves in the park on an autumn morning can lead to a sorting session indoors. You can make piles of leaves that are muddy and not muddy, leaves that are round shapes and leaves that are long, leaves you like and those you don't. The groups do not matter – it is the sorting and discussion that are the useful activities. Twigs, stones, shells, beads, buttons, socks, toy bricks, toy vehicles, farm animals all lend themselves to simple sorting activities. (Remember to stay aware of safety if you are using small items with under-threes or any children who like to put objects in their mouths.)

Many of the words used in sorting will be mathematical. Sorting and grouping is a mathematical activity.

If you like to count, you can count the contents of your groups too. If the difference in group sizes is pronounced, it may be useful to point out that there are '*lots more* leaves in this group' or that 'this group has *less than* the other one'.

In the early stages of using the spoken word children begin to show an

Collecting leaves ready for sorting.

understanding of the rules of the language they are learning. In English one of the first rules that often appears is using 's' on the end of a word to show 'more than one' of something. This can be one of the first signs that a child understands the idea of the number *one* and the idea of *more than one*. Very often the adding 's' rule is applied indiscriminately, e.g. one pig, lots of pigs; one sheep, lots of 'sheeps'. The English may not be perfect but the maths behind it shows significant understanding of the idea of 'one' and 'more than one'.

Using books

Often, when reading books with young children, we think purely about the enjoyment of the story and, if we are interested in our children's learning, the more obvious educational content especially the pictures and the conversations we can have based on them. Old favourites, such as *We're Going on a Bear Hunt* by Michael Rosen and Helen Oxenbury, are wonderful vehicles for active participation in interpreting *over*, *under* and *through*, for example.

'We're going on a bear hunt' – *over, under* and *through.*

There are also mathematical aspects to using books with young children that are less apparent. Many stories for young children have strong sequences. In the early days of using books, children often turn to any page and expect you to read from there, or even to go backwards. However, when a child is used to looking at the whole book from start to finish and is familiar with the conventional layout of books, they will automatically open the book at the beginning. Even 18-month-old toddlers who come from reading-rich environments will do this with their favourite books. An awareness of sequence in using books begins early.

We turn the pages of a book *one by one*. We start with the *first* page, we turn over the *next one*. We go *forwards* or *backwards* through the book, and these words are defined in relation to the *start* and *finish*. The book is *large* or *small*. 'Big book' versions of standard-sized ones make this distinction very clearly. Some books have *lots* of pages, some have only a *few*. The story has a clear *ending* and when we reach that we *stop*. The structure of a book can be described mathematically.

Children whose home languages are those other than English may have encountered books that read in the opposite direction to the conventions in English books. If you are not a reader of the child's home language yourself, find out the reading conventions and, if possible, talk about the differences in the conventions with the child. A child who is being brought up in a bilingual environment with different reading conventions will have to sort out those differences in their own mind, and you can help.

Some children's book illustrators have distinctive, recognisable styles. Korky Paul's illustrations (*Winnie the Witch*, for example) are easily identified as his; likewise Jane Hissey's *Old Bear* books could only have been done by her. One two-year-old we know was very familiar with the book *Simpkin* by Quentin Blake. Whenever she sees Quentin Blake illustrations in other books she calls them 'Simpkin'. She is familiar enough with the style to be able to group all pictures by the same illustrator in this way. Identification of illustrative style demands a high level of pattern recognition. It is worth nothing, also, that shape recognition is very important in developing reading skills. The 'whole word' reading method depends on the child's ability to distinguish word shapes and this method plays an essential part in learning to read, even when phonics are used as the main approach to teaching reading.

Recognition of individual letter forms as being representative of sounds is a symbolic and abstract idea. Similarly, in maths the written squiggles called by individual number names are abstract representations of physical amounts. The connection between the abstract squiggle and what it represents is beyond the understanding of most two- to three-year-olds. However, the recognition of a squiggle as a number name is manageable if there is a reason for it: some two-year-olds are able to find channels on the television using a remote control and pressing the correct number, including a number suggested by an adult. They will be recognising the shape of the written figure, not connecting it with a quantity. Likewise, children on their third birthday may point to a '3' on their birthday card and name the figure 'three'. It is, after all, an interestingly shaped squiggle and easily differentiated from others. It may seem to them to have something to do with presents, not with having been born three years earlier.

Colour

Pre-school activities such as sorting shapes, threading beads in a sequence and printing patterns all require an ability to discriminate between different colours. A pre-school child who hasn't grasped the concept of colour and cannot reliably identify primary colours may be hampered in their development of mathematical understanding.

The first colour many young children identify is yellow. It is often described by parents and carers as the child's 'favourite colour'. Clearly it is a very bright colour and commands attention. Also, it is more often seen as a true colour rather than a shade. All the things you call 'yellow' are very close to a single colour. There is more of a range with, for example, shades of reds or blues. As yellow is so often the colour that most interests young children, try to show and name plenty of yellow objects but also introduce other primary colours to help the general concept of colour to be understood.

Clothes provide a good opportunity for discussing colour. Many young children become inseparable from their bright red wellies. Looking for things of the same colour as their clothes will help a child to begin the difficult task of understanding this concept. A two-year-old will be able to 'help' to sort the clean washing. Searching for socks can be a very useful exercise in matching colours – and matching patterns too.

Learning about colour takes a lot of experience. When a child is learning to name animals they have to work out the similarities and differences between all animals. Similarly, a child's brain has to sort out exactly which property it is that objects have in common every time you speak a colour word. Is it the shape, the texture, the taste, the way you use the object? Is it to do with its size or position or is it something else? Colour is not a straightforward concept to understand.

It is just as hard to build up a concept of number. The child is confronted with the word 'one', perhaps with reference to 'one spoonful', 'one sock' or 'one book'. The first thing that will happen is that the brain will try to identify some shared physical quality between all these things labelled 'one'. The brain needs to know what type of category 'one' belongs to. Does it, for example, relate to size, shape, colour or the type of object? All this helps to show why it takes so long for young children to begin to understand the concept of number and why it is extremely useful to introduce counting in as many different contexts as possible.

Summary

- Sorting and grouping is a mathematical activity.
- Adding 's' to the ending of a plural noun can be one of the first signs that a child understands the idea of the number 'one' and the idea of 'more than one'.
- The practicalities of reading books involve concepts of direction, position, size, number and sequence.
- Recognition of pattern and shape is a pre-reading skill. It is essential for identification of letter and number forms and whole word shapes in later years.
- In a similar way to learning about the abstract nature of colour, understanding the concept of number is challenging for young children. Making sense of colour and number can take a very long time.

The language of counting

Learning to count

Knowing the names of the numbers is not the same as counting. If we are to count any five objects we have to know:

- the words *one, two, three, four, five*
- the fixed order that these numbers go in
- that *one* matches just one object, *two* matches two objects (any two objects), and so on
- that we count each item only once
- that if we are starting to count a new group we begin with the word *one*
- that the final number we reach when counting one thing at a time is the number of things in the whole group
- that the objects can be counted in any order
- that the five objects will always be five, providing none are removed or added
- that we can count by touching items, moving items, or just looking at items (and actually we do not even have to see them – sounds can be counted too)
- that counting can be applied to any objects in any situation: the counting process is always the same.

This is quite a lot to comprehend. It is likely that, even if a two-year-old can recite the numbers up to ten or more, they will not have made sense of the concepts listed above. Most children of reception class age will know the number sequence to ten but some will still not understand the process of counting objects.

In order to make sense of counting, it is useful for a child to hear the activity used in as many different ways as possible: the more ways they see counting applied and start to use it themselves, the better they will understand it. As we mentioned in the last chapter, we can start this very young, if it happens in a natural way. There is no point in forcing it.

We can recite, sing, tell stories about and play with the names of numbers and the counting sequence. We can help two- and three-year-olds become familiar with the first two items on the list above: number names and the sequence they go in. A list of useful books is given in Appendix 1.

We can count the quantities of things in our environment: people, animals, toys, vehicles, trees, food, books, birds, plants, our breathing, actions, fingers and toes, everyday objects, the sun, moon and stars! The rest of the list above will begin to make sense over time and through endless application. Children may be five or six before they really understand – they cannot be hurried and there are no short cuts although, as we have seen, there are plenty of ways we can facilitate their understanding.

Children who have home languages other than English can be encouraged to learn number names, the number sequences and to count in these languages at home and in other childcare settings. In nurseries, if there are no speakers of the home languages on the staff, try to involve parents and carers in helping children learn the words and sequences in the home languages. You may want to learn them too. Early counting books in translation may be available through the library services, specialist teachers resources centres or through mail order with the Letterbox Library (see Appendix 3).

ACTIVITY

Start your own list of books, stories, rhymes and songs that are useful for explaining and exploring the number sequence (from low to high numbers) and counting upwards (e.g. from one to five or ten). We are only able to give a small selection of what is available (see Appendices) and there are many resources around.

Summary

- Knowing the names of numbers is not the same as being able to count. However, it is essential to know them, and the order in which they go, as part of the process of counting.
- Counting quantities involves many skills and levels of understanding about abstract ideas. It can take many years to make sense of it.
- It is useful for a child to hear the number sequence and counting used in as many different ways as possible in real life, songs, stories and rhymes.
- Ensure that children in your care who have home languages other than English are supported and have access to resources for learning the names of numbers, the counting sequence and how to count in their home languages too.

The need to help and be involved

Two- and three-year-olds enjoy joining in with real, everyday activities and their involvement is important. They have a growing need to be included in a practical way in the jobs they see in the world around them and many real activities have a clear mathematical content.

For example, when we do the laundry we *sort* clothes and put clean washing into piles. We *match* socks together and *count* them to make *pairs*. In making beds we use positional words: tucking *under*, pulling *over*, putting *in* or *on*. Even young children can hold the *edges* of pillow cases and towels while we fold them. We fold the towels in *half* and we match the *edges* together. These are all potentially complicated ideas but are part of mainstream maths and can be introduced through everyday activities.

We count fasteners as we do them up on the duvet covers. Similarly, giving a child the peg bag to count *one*, *two* or *three* pegs at a time to help you while you peg out the wet washing keeps them busy and involved and engaged in an important activity.

Here are more ideas and none of them need special equipment:

TIDYING UP

- sorting different toys into baskets and boxes or books on shelves according to their size; taking objects back to the rooms in which they belong

- matching shoes and boots in pairs by the door; counting toys into boxes and sorting out the shopping – all the tins together, all the apples in one bowl, the pears and bananas in another etc.

CLEANING

- using words to describe shapes and surfaces – cleaning round the edges, wiping the surfaces, washing the square tiles on the kitchen floor
- using words to describe position – brushing under, putting things on top of others out of the way, wiping high up or low down
- counting the shelves as we dust or wipe them; counting the plastic mugs as the child washes them in the sink and puts them out to dry
- filling a bucket with water – how full should you make it?

COOKING AND MEALTIMES

- measuring out spoonfuls; pouring out liquids (Do we need more? Have we enough? Is there too much?)
- adding ingredients together
- rolling out pastry (How thick or thin?); cutting out shapes with pastry cutters (How many can we make?)
- counting prepared vegetables as they are put in the pan; counting the spoons as you lay the table – one for each person's pudding
- playing with weights on balance scales – first experiments with weighing.

GARDENING

- watering plants (how full is your watering can?) If you are a gardener, a child-sized watering can for the children who help you is a sensible purchase)
- counting seedlings as they are planted in the ground; making a hole big enough to fit each one
- washing and stacking flowerpots – put the biggest ones together, stack the small ones
- picking fresh fruit and vegetables in season (try a visit to a 'pick your own' farm). Even growing cress on a windowsill can lead to discussions about rate of growth and heights of seedlings.

The two-year-old in the photograph was sent into the garden on his own to collect cherry tomatoes for lunch. The childminder had shown him what was needed. He had to work out which were red and which were green and leave the green ones on the plants (he couldn't name the colours, but was able to discriminate which was which). He picked some, went back to

Selecting the tomatoes for lunch.

check with her and she sent him back to pick some more. It was a complicated job – involving a lot of thinking, sorting by colour and estimation of amounts – and moreover it was a real help in the lunch-time preparations. He knew it.

Books such as Sarah Garland's *Doing the Garden*, *Doing the Washing* or *Going Shopping* reinforce the language of everyday activities and discussions about them can include words with a mathematical content.

ACTIVITY

Think about going on a shopping trip with an active two-year-old. See if you can make a list, similar to the above, of some of the types of mathematical activities and conversations using mathematical words that you might have.

Summary

- Everyday activities can involve children in simple practical applications of maths in housework, shopping, cooking and gardening.
- Allowing children to help enables them to assimilate the ideas and language in a real and valuable way.

Developments in play

Most two-year-olds enjoy playing alongside other people but not necessarily with them. However, some activities do involve co-operation with others.

Some play equipment can only be used if it is shared: the children need to go *one at a time* on the slide in the toddler group; one child goes *first* on the little trampoline, their friend goes *second*, someone else goes *third*. There are plenty of mathematical examples where co-operation is concerned.

Children start to enjoy imaginative play and simple role-play. The toy train is driven along the carpet to 'Grandma's house' past a couple of landmarks that the child remembers from journeys in real life. Events in the sequence of a real journey may be recalled. The child may begin to use descriptive words to add to their play: 'Up the hill' or 'Stop at the shops'.

Role-play that copies adult activities starts to be popular and you may start to hear words and phrases being said which you yourself have used. The child picks up a doll and says 'Up you come', 'Go to sleep now' or 'Let's go up to bed'. The child mimics actions that have been done to them and copies the words too.

Pretend tea parties are a favourite activity for this age group. A set of plastic cups, saucers, plates and some cutlery has great play value. Mathematically it has enormous potential. Are there enough cups for all the dolls? Can they each have a cup and a saucer? Can you match the red cup with the red saucer? Can you give each doll some raisins and a paper biscuit? When playing 'sharing out' games with toddlers, keep the number of things small – only two or three to start with. Point out when a doll has no items on its plate. Sometimes start your counting from zero.

Creative role-play is developed much more during the remaining pre-school years. It is easy to resource children's role-play at home: a cardboard box becomes a ship; an adult's woolly hat and shopping bag turns a child instantly into a postal worker; the childminder's cycle helmet magically creates an astronaut. Playgroups and nurseries provide many opportunities to engage in role-play and as children get older they learn to play more with others and communicate with them while doing so. In this way, many opportunities arise where children can share mathematical language and ideas with others.

Summary

- There are plenty of opportunities for using mathematical language when co-operative play is taking place.
- Children start to mimic adults' words and actions in role-play including using, in context, the mathematical expressions that they have heard.
- Some popular activities, such as pretend tea parties, have much mathematical potential.
- More sophisticated role-play presents the opportunity to explore using mathematical ideas and language and to share these with other children.

3

The Foundations of Maths:
Developing Pre-school Skills

As in all areas of children's learning and development, we aim for ideals in early maths learning that will stand them in good stead for later work. We try to help children to develop their natural curiosity and creativity, their ability to explore, discover and repeatedly test out their ideas. We try to encourage them to be increasingly confident in tackling problems of all kinds and provide them with reliable support so that they know that their requests for help or information will be treated seriously. All the time, we try to help them with the words they need to communicate. Everything they do reinforces the idea that there is a good reason for learning. All their learning at home, in playgroup or nursery and in later years will be strengthened by these foundations.

This chapter looks at how these aims are applied to children's learning between about three and five years of age. The majority of children will attend some sort of playgroup or nursery during this time and this chapter focuses on mathematical activities in these types of setting. However, as in Chapter 2, in most instances the ideas discussed are easily transferable between the home and professional care environments.

Attendance at nursery, even full-time, will probably only occupy the minority of a young child's week and learning at home obviously continues in parallel. Childcare workers play an important role in helping parents to realise the mathematical content of the activities they do at home with their children. Mathematically confident parents may have lots to offer other parents and professionals too. Two-way dialogue can help everyone.

We have encountered a dilemma in writing this chapter. If you were to track a young child's busy session at nursery it would be difficult to pull out exclusively mathematical activities. As in real life, maths in the early years setting gets everywhere. It should do because it is part of everything! However, professional carers working in grant-aided environments are expected to provide a curriculum that aims to satisfy mathematical criteria (e.g. the *Early Learning Goals*, introduced in September 2000, see Appendix 2) which are listed as separate from other areas of the curriculum. We have resolved the dilemma of whether to write this chapter linked to more formal goals or whether to structure it around the play-oriented environment of most early years settings by doing a bit of both. Many early years' providers will find themselves doing the same in their own planning work.

Precise, pre-determined goals must not be seen as a complete list of the mathematical learning that is possible. They are a tiny fraction of it and they must be integrated back into a much wider curriculum. There is a lot of planning and structure behind the free-play and fun that is visible in a nursery or playgroup. Good practice includes planning for curiosity, creativity, exploration, discovery, experimenting, problem solving and language learning. Precise learning goals can be met in this environment.

Maths can be learnt in every physical part of the nursery setting: the outdoor play areas, the garden, the external fabric of the building, the indoor rooms, the walls, the cloakrooms, the use of kitchen facilities, the corridors and the area in the street or land immediately around the site. Given that many early years settings are pushed for space, it makes sense to use every corner available.

This was an experience recounted by a playgroup assistant who was reminded that cooking and making food are some of the richest mathematical activities anyone can do with young children.

'Five children in our group made some sandwiches indoors. The maths of making a sandwich is quite considerable. They counted *two* slices of bread each and spread them with margarine, covering the uppermost *surface* of the bread, right to the *edges* with butter. They chose jam or cheese to put *inside* and spread the filling *on* the buttered bread. They put the *second* piece of bread *on top* so that the filling was *in between* the two slices. They cut their sandwiches into *triangles*, *rectangles* or *squares* and put them into little paper bags to take outside.

We got the binoculars the children had made earlier from cardboard tubes. Then we walked in a long line in and out of the bushes pretending to be explorers on an expedition. We followed each other around the playground and the children decided to hide in the garden playhouse where we took turns in looking for wild animals out of the window while we ate the sandwiches. One of the boys spotted a poster that was the same shape as his sandwich and soon all the children were hunting for triangles, squares and rectangles with their binoculars. I asked them if there were any wild animals that looked like those shapes. We wondered about elephants' ears. We talked about how interesting it was to look for triangles through the circular ends of the 'binoculars'. It was interesting to see where we ended up, given that we had started with sandwiches. I made a mental note to find a book about elephants – maybe one of the *Elmer* ones (by David McKee) – for story time'.

The early years curriculum is not sorted into small compartments; maths doesn't happen sitting quietly at a desk in between recreational or meal breaks. It isn't tidy but it is often unexpected, exciting and funny. It shows us what all learning could be like. The playgroup assistant in the example quoted above, while having a lot of fun and going along with the children's own involvement in the role-play, could still produce a written account of the mathematical learning that had taken place.

ACTIVITY

Observe children engaged in role-play together. Write up the maths content of what you see. Can you identify a story book that you could have read to the children afterwards which would have helped draw out some of the mathematical ideas from their role-play?

The children in the example were helped to use the appropriate mathematical language that they needed in their activities. A major role for all teaching staff is to enable children to find the right word at the right time. The language children use enables them to make sense of what they are experiencing and record it in words in their minds. As children's mathematical language develops it becomes more and more exact. The formal mathematical use of certain words is very precise.

Early years workers can encourage children's exploration of language and how it is applied. One four-year-old was sitting playing on a flat, carpeted corner on the stair turn at the bottom of the staircase in his childminder's house. He asked her to bring a box of bricks over to him: 'Put it on the . . .', he searched for the word to describe the place where he was sitting. '. . . On the surface', he tried. It was a lovely word to find and they were able to extend the conversation, talking about names for parts of stairs and where you could find 'surfaces'.

Summary

- Maths is everywhere in the early years environment. It is part of every aspect of the curriculum and can be learnt in every physical part of the building and outdoor areas.
- Precise pre-determined goals for children's mathematical learning must not be seen as a complete list of the mathematical learning possibilities. They are a tiny fraction of it and must be integrated back into a much wider curriculum.
- Cooking and making food are some of the richest mathematical activities anyone can do with young children.
- A major role for all teaching staff is to enable children to find the right words for communicating at the times they are needed.

Familiar activities

Comparing and matching

The group of children in the previous example were also being encouraged to observe their surroundings. The outdoors is wonderful for finding things to look at, insects and other mini-beasts in particular. Comparing the size of two beetles, or the colours and patterns on butterflies, is something we do instinctively. Observing the little differences between creatures helps us to appreciate the natural world even more. Young children are drawn to small details in the environment and we can encourage that enthusiasm.

We can compare and match things in many different ways:

- by length, width, height, thickness and overall size
- by colour (for real detail, try looking at paint manufacturer's colour charts)
- by quantity
- by texture, pattern and other physical attributes.

Matching quantities is important in helping to understand one-to-one correspondence (where one number equates to one object). It is the basis of counting, but we do not have to use numbers. We match things equally or unequally all the time.

- Laying the table for nursery lunch may involve putting cutlery and a beaker on the table beside each chair: 'Is there a place setting for each chair?' 'Have we enough mugs?'
- Tidying up the peg boards at the end of play will mean putting one peg in each hole: 'Have we found all the pegs?' 'Are there any missing?'
- Helping put out the paints means matching one brush to each pot of paint.
- Tidying up the felt-tip pens means matching one (correctly coloured) cap to each pen.
- There are many manufactured toys and games that use matching as a central activity, e.g. snap.

Sorting

This is another of those activities that we do all the time, particularly when tidying up. Labelling boxes for materials with a picture of the contents as well as the words helps non-readers be equally involved in this kind of sorting.

There are many ways of providing opportunities for more discussion about sorting.

- We can sort buttons and coins, shape tiles, natural materials, photographs, toy animals, vehicles or toy people.
- We can sort things into groups linked to the materials the objects are made from, the uses to which the objects are put or the places the objects are used.
- We can sort things into groups linked to particular attributes such as pattern, colour or whether the object behaves in a certain way, e.g. rolls or flies.
- We can sort things because of the letter sound they begin with, or whether they appear in a story or nursery rhyme or not.
- We can sort things based on whether we like or dislike them. In a group setting everyone's choices might be different. This automatically leads into discussions about respecting other people's choices and celebrating differences between people.

A C T I V I T Y

Make a set of picture cards of objects (e.g. food, toys, items of clothing) and help a group of children sort them into order of preference. Is it possible to find common agreement? If not, how can you make everyone feel good about their choices?

Sequencing and ordering

Very often children will find sequences in toys or educational games without prompting. A child will play with a baby doll, waking it up and then going through a role-play of the sequence of a day until bedtime. A child will build a sequence of steps out of Duplo, or other toy bricks, putting columns in order of height. Sequences in percussion rhythms can be copied as can small combinations of dance steps. Children can retell the sequence of a story.

Children may put measuring beakers in size order, copy colours in the order of the rainbow, arrange all the farm animals in order of fatness. See if a group of six to ten children can arrange themselves in height order without an adult's help.

'We assembled a collection of six or seven different kinds of clothes pegs. It included wooden dolly pegs and "gypsy" pegs and different coloured plastic designs. A group of five children spent a whole hour talking about the difference and similarities, sorting them according to different criteria: wood and plastic, containing metal and no metal, old and new, and so on. We made sequences and patterns with them, talked about the history of pegs and how they were made. We tested all the pegs to see which was best for pegging dolls' clothes on a toy washing line. We counted them and clipped them to each other in long lines to see how long they could become. I hadn't planned for the activity to take this long, but they were enjoying it so much we didn't want to stop.'

Puzzles and board games

We will continue to mention puzzles and board games throughout this book. They are popular with children because they are clearly equated with play.

With games children learn to take turns in a particular order, to follow sequences (e.g. shake a dice, count the spots, move a piece), to count and move according to the score on a dice, to match identical cards and to collect a set or group of something. Some of the best games have been around for a long time: happy families, snap, donkey, ladybird, beetle, snakes and ladders or ludo. Playing these might link well with discussions about the types of toys and games parents and grandparents enjoyed when young (linking with developing a sense of history). There are many other board games produced for use in early years' settings.

'Dominoes' needs a particular mention. The game is very useful for counting, matching and starting to add. The traditional game with spotty dominoes matches one domino to another that has already been put on the table. However, it is also possible to play it using addition where every join must add up to six. This game is too challenging for many younger children, but may be very useful for the older ones who have an understanding of simple addition. (Dominoes with only pictures on them are also available, offering a good matching game without the numerical component).

Jigsaws, of varying degrees of difficulty, help children to develop their spatial skills. You can make up simple ten- to twenty-piece jigsaws from children's drawings or from enlarged photos of playgroup activities.

ACTIVITY

Take a look at some of the children's board games on the market and try designing one with a particular child in mind. You could use their favourite toys as 'counters', e.g. some dolls' house people or toy cars. Keep it simple, with a 'start' and a 'finish', and use a dice to generate the numbers of spaces to move. Play the game with the child.

Shape, colour and pattern

Activities linked to shape, colour and pattern are favourites in childcare settings, probably because they link so strongly to artwork and modelling.

Printing, particularly with hands and feet, is very popular (and, of course, on a hand print you can count the fingers on your hand and match them to those on the print – the same with toes). Children can be encouraged to find objects in the natural world that might make interesting shapes, for example acorn cups print little circles. Everyone is familiar with vegetable printing and potatoes may be cut into all kinds of two-dimensional geometric shapes to be used for printing sequences. Use till rolls to make long sequences of prints for borders for artwork.

Look at patterns in nature. The patterns made by the clouds in the sky, on animal skins, fur and camouflage, the V-shapes made by birds migrating, or

Measuring and fitting shapes in junk modelling.

the dappled shade made by the sun shining through the leaves of a large tree – all may generate wonderful discussions. Children's own pictures of animals may include the patterns: blotchy giraffes, spotty leopards or striped fish. Our clothes are usually a rich source of colour and pattern and they are worth describing and drawing too.

Junk modelling and simple woodwork are important because they allow children the opportunity to create in a more flexible way than is allowed for by most construction toys. Children design their own ideas beforehand in their own minds, or invent and change things as they go along. It uses lots of imagination to turn a cereal box into a tractor but young children do it all the time. They refine their fine motor skills as they cut, stick, hammer and decorate. They work out, in three dimensions, how shapes fit together.

Children can learn the names of two- and three-dimensional shapes, preferably when they are familiar with the forms through play. Often the names of three-dimensional shapes are not explained to young children but there is no reason why a child should not be given words such as 'cube', 'cylinder', 'pyramid' or 'sphere', if they are interested. Playing with bricks is a

Exploring shape and position with your whole body.

good way to explore the nature of solid forms, as is drawing and cutting out shapes. Remember to look for the patterns made by real bricks on the outside walls of buildings. Can you copy the pattern in Duplo or other toy bricks?

Symmetry also falls into this category. Folding paper into half, quarters or sixths, and snipping away small shapes from the edges leads to unfolding beautiful butterflies, snowflakes and other interesting discoveries. Paint blots on paper and fold it when the paint is still wet to make more symmetrical patterns. Use safe mirrors to turn half-patterns back into whole ones and look at symmetry in leaves, children's drawings and photos of faces.

Awareness of shape and form is not just created by small-scale indoor play. It is generated during outdoor play too. Remember that the outdoor environment needs to be planned as carefully as the indoor one because it is so central to children's play and learning. Much mathematical learning and development is possible outside.

When a child plays on a traditional swing, the frame has triangular ends and

Fitting yourself inside a circular shape – and it rolls!

they get a sense of the stability of the shape. Sliding down a slide helps them feel, with their whole body, what a gradient is like. A climbing frame is full of four-sided shapes which a child can stand on, wriggle through and hang from. A tunnel for crawling through can be rolled in – it fits a child's body perfectly. A huge ball is impossible to balance on – it won't stay still long enough. Curves, zig-zags, waves, loops and straight lines can be painted on a tarmac surface for running along and balancing on.

Obstacle courses can be made in the playground, or indoors in bad weather. Include blocks and crates to balance on, beams to crawl along and tunnels to crawl through. Repeated over and over they become sequences that the child feels with their whole body. Numbers or colours can be incorporated too e.g. ask them to step, in number order, on crates numbered one to five, or only to step on the blue ones.

Being able to explore shapes, inside and out, using the whole body, is what learning about geometry needs to be for three-, four- or five-year-olds.

There are many rhymes, songs and stories that link to ideas about shape, colour and pattern. *Elmer* by David McKee is ideal for drawing out these ideas. *The Blue Balloon* by Mick Inkpen is excellent material for looking at colours and shapes. Songs and rhymes with lots of repetition create musical patterns which children can add to with sequences of percussion instrument rhythms.

Train sets

These are very useful aids to shape, space and positional words. Make sure that girls get space to play with them as well as boys. Constructing the track uses language about straight lines and curves. Closing a curved loop into one that is continuous is a difficult, spatially advanced mathematical activity and a real test of problem solving. Building bridges and tunnels uses positional words. Carriages are counted and engines go *first* with carriages *behind* them.

Patterns and time

It will be a while before children of this age start to develop a sense of time but there are things that help to highlight the cyclical nature of the natural world and these will give a sense of time passing. Watching frogs or chicks through the hatching, growing and changing parts of their life cycles is relatively quick and dramatic enough for it to mean something. Planting sunflowers in the spring and watching them grow from one tiny seed until they are huge, with new seeds that can be harvested in the autumn term, is a lovely (but longer) cycle to follow. Celebrating birthdays and festivals gives a sense of time passing.

ACTIVITY

Another cyclical pattern, which is worth observing when children are taken out on a shopping expedition, is the way traffic lights change. Stand safely, well back from the lights and the road and watch. Can the children work out the pattern? Can they work out what the instructions must be for the traffic when each combination of lights is seen? You have to hope that no one jumps the red light when you are watching!

Role-play

This has already been mentioned several times but it is so central to children's play at this age that another aspect needs highlighting. As children become confident with mathematical terms and using numbers you will hear them being integrated smoothly into their role-play games.

Role play: using mathematical language to organise a party.

The children in the play phone box in the photo on the previous page were engaged in a complicated game which involved phoning a catering firm's fictious phone number dictated by one child to another who dialled it. The call began 'I'm having a party this Sunday. Can you make the food for it? It's for nineteen, no twenty people. Can you bring the food at three o'clock?' The children took 'notes' of their call too. Such confident use of words to do with numbers, time and dates indicated real confidence with the material.

Children use mathematical language frequently when playing shops or cafés. Making food, real or pretend, from paper and cardboard or playdough, to sell in the 'shop' extends the play still further. Children buy quantities of things, count them, weight them and share them out.

Money

Toy money is practical for play shopping: real money is even better (if impractical in a group situation). Children can be encouraged to make coin

Concentrating on counting pennies in long rows.

rubbings that can be stuck onto card to make play money. The detailed observation that goes alongside making a coin rubbing is very useful.

Occasionally it is possible for young children to see and handle large quantities of money. The children in the photograph were engaged in a money-raising event for charity. Everyone was asked to bring in a little bag of pennies which were laid out in continuous lines. Lots of counting went on and the quantity of pennies arranged by thirty children was considerable. It was a practical way to present the idea of a huge number.

Summary

- Comparing, matching, sorting, sequencing, ordering and junk modelling are all mathematical activities familiar in early years settings, as are activities looking at symmetry, shape and pattern.
- Games and puzzles use counting, matching, grouping and spatial skills.
- Awareness of shape and form is generated during outdoor as well as indoor play.
- Looking at cyclical patterns helps with an initial understanding of time.
- As children become confident with mathematical terms and using numbers you will hear these being integrated smoothly into their role-play games.
- Handling real money as well as toy money is helpful.

Numbers and counting

Different ways of using numbers

Numbers can be used as **nominal** numbers (labels such as bus numbers or phone numbers), as **ordinal** numbers (*first, second, third*) or **cardinal** numbers (*one, two, three* etc., which are actually used to count a quantity in a set).

All these ways of using numbers are explored through play and observation. We have already mentioned that rhymes, songs and stories are particularly good ways to learn the counting sequence upwards or downwards, but they are also useful in helping to learn about adding numbers together simply or about subtraction. *This Little Puffin* (ed. Elizabeth Matterson) and *My Oxford 123 Number Rhyme Book* are good places to begin to find material to use in group time, but there are many books of this kind being published.

If you are working with very young children on the counting sequence that goes from one to ten, then it is important that the rhymes and songs you use follow that direction: *1, 2, 3, 4, 5 – once I caught a fish alive . . .* would be appropriate because it counts upwards; *Ten Green Bottles* would not because the counting sequence goes downwards which might be confusing. Similarly, you might not want to include songs that use calculations with more complicated numbers, although these might be enormously useful with older children. The BEAM book *Learning Mathematics in the Nursery: Desirable Approaches* contains a useful section that groups number rhymes and songs according to these types of criteria.

ACTIVITY

Add to your own list of useful number rhymes that you started in Chapter 2 – you will refer to them often when you work with young children. Make a note of the sorts of number work that are covered.

Using your fingers, and encouraging children to do the same while you sing, is very helpful in all number songs. In more complicated rhymes such as *Ten fat sausages sizzling in the pan. One went pop and another went bang . . .* you can bend over a finger (a sausage) on each hand with each verse, then count the fingers left on each hand and then the total. This gives a useful visual introduction to the sums 5 + 5, 4 + 4, 3 + 3, 2 + 2, and 1 + 1.

Children need lots of practice in counting in as many situations as possible. They need to understand that a number of objects stays the same regardless of the arrangement they are placed in (**conservation of number**), and this understanding comes through lots of practice in manipulation of objects. The child in the photo was arranging and counting play people on the dolls' house furniture in different combinations. She was testing out this principle in play.

This same practice in arranging and rearranging will help to build a foundation for the idea that if you put two apples in a bowl, then three apples, this will give you the same total as if you put them in the other way round, in other words: 2 + 3 = 3 + 2. It is a fundamental law in pure mathematics.

Guesswork and estimation

Children also need lots of practice in guesswork and estimation. Accurate estimation is useful because it helps to avoid generating ridiculous answers to calculations later. Showing children a small group of objects and inviting guesses to the quantity before you then check with careful counting

Arranging and counting play people.

encourages sensible guesswork. It also helps children be content with the idea of being approximately right or good enough, which has an important place in maths – not all answers have to be exact. As children get older you can offer bigger and bigger quantities of things to guess. Make guesses yourself – demonstrate that sensible estimation is fine.

Reading numbers

Learning to read symbolic, abstract squiggles – the written representations of numbers – takes time. Frequently pre-school children learn '3' and '4' from recognising the numbers on their birthday cards. They also learn other siblings' ages and their house or flat number early on. The first abstract figures to be learnt need to have a real-life meaning too.

Sometimes playgroups and nurseries use counting and number recognition when the children are together in small groups. Everyone may count the children present at the start of the day and one child chooses a number card to match which is stuck on a chart showing how many children are there.

That information may be consulted at snack time to remember how many drinks or biscuits are needed.

Some nurseries and playgroups put a limit on the maximum number of children allowed at a particular activity, e.g. the water or sand tables. The number is displayed beside the activity so that the children can be aware of it and monitor the situation themselves.

Recording numbers

Some children may spontaneously want to learn to write symbolic numbers, others may be interested in keeping records in other ways. Learning to count a set of objects and then to make the same number of marks on paper to represent the amount is called **tallying**, a means of recording quantities that is thousands of years old. Other children may use pictures to represent their mathematical thinking. This child clearly drew a picture of a person holding up five fingers and a matching quantity of objects (cakes in this instance). It shows a very logical approach to recording quantity at the pre-writing stage.

Numbers in children's drawings: a person with five fingers and five cakes.

Children may also find it easy to understand simple pictorial charts and graphs. Simple, life-size bar charts of each child's height, with their name clearly written on their 'bar', show clearly who is tallest, who is next and so on.

Children's drawings often give good indications of whether a child is ready to write letters and numbers. Careful drawings with a degree of detail usually indicate that the child has good enough co-ordination and pencil control. If written numbers are to be taught, it will help children to learn to write their shapes using many different materials, everything from soapy bubbles to mud as well as pencil.

Measuring

Pre-school children tend to include measuring activities as part of their spontaneous play. Pouring water between containers and filling buckets and boxes with sand are seen in most early years settings. Words such as *full* and *empty*, *more* and *less* are used frequently in conversations and can be

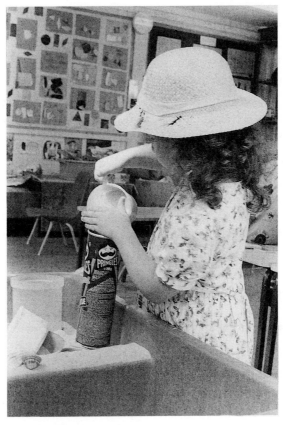

Carefully measuring sand in different containers.

encouraged. Sometimes it can be fun to play with large quantities of dried foods: couscous or rice pour well but feel different. Local shops may be able to let you have split packets free of charge.

Weighing is another activity that fascinates. If possible, find balance scales and child-safe weights in a range of sizes. Encourage weighing of everything. Set a challenge: 'What is the funniest thing you can find to weigh?' 'Can you find something beginning with 's' to weigh?' 'Can you make the scales balance with some play people on one side and some toy animals on the other?' Weighing of ingredients may also be possible when cooking.

Distance can be measured in all kinds of ways. Children can practise using non-standard measurements: in hands, feet, strides, body-lengths, teddies, sticks, bricks and conkers. They need to get the idea of measuring using a unit of some kind to enable comparisons but do not need to meet metres, kilograms or litres just yet.

This piece of work illustrates, once again, how children can be encouraged in mathematical activity while doing one of the things they enjoy best. 'It was a really hot day and the children were making mud pies in the garden. We decided to find out how to make a recipe for the best mud pie mix. We took a large washing-up bowl and counted cups of water and mud, keeping a careful tally of both scratched in the ground beside us. Eventually we decided that we had found the best mix: not too dry or runny. We then split the mixture in to three equal parts, moulded one into a squashy mud pie straight away and added cups of grass clippings to another and sand from the sandpit to the third mix. We let them dry a bit and decided that the grass clippings mix was the best. When we went indoors, we wrote up our recipe with pictures of cups of water, mud and grass to show quantities in case anyone else wanted to try it. It was very mathematical and scientific – and very, very grubby – but great fun.'

Maths for pre-school children should be fun, and it should also mean something to them. There needs to be a reason for their mathematical activity and often this is incidental to their play. Teaching staff and adult helpers can watch carefully and give a helping hand with ideas of things to try or useful words to describe something.

Good general planning and provision of resources, combined with attentive and aware adults on hand to help, will mean that children play in an environment that can be rich in mathematical learning.

Summary

- Rhymes, songs and stories are useful ways to learn number sequences and simple addition and subtraction in a fun way.
- Accurate estimation is an important mathematical skill.
- Early years settings can provide good, practical reasons to count and recognise numbers.
- Children can represent numbers in different ways, e.g. pictorially or by tallying, as well as by learning to write symbolic numbers when they are developmentally ready to do so.
- The measuring of volume, distance and weight is easily applied to play activities.
- A well-planned nursery or playgroup will be rich in mathematical learning opportunities.

4

Challenges in Early Maths Education

The curriculum and formal work

In recent years there has been an increasing interest in the content of the curriculum used in playgroups and nursery settings. There is ongoing discussion about the goals for early years learning, and what these might mean, both in general and when applied to individual subject areas in the pre-school curriculum. Initially it sounds wise to dovetail pre-school learning with the requirements of the National Curriculum.

Although rigorous thinking about the content and aims of any learning activity seems wise, we think that there is also a danger in linking early years work too tightly with a curriculum for older children. Younger children's learning is focused strongly on acquiring skills and understanding through play. That of older children in the mainstream state school system is more formal and structured. We have heard some teachers and parents say that, since the introduction of the National Curriculum with its focus on the formal learning of literacy and numeracy, the curriculum seems to have narrowed and is too goal-orientated rather than being developmentally appropriate. They have commented that opportunities for creative, play-based learning have all but disappeared, even for the youngest Key Stage 1 children in school.

In some cases this may filter downwards into early years provision. The temptation to teach in a more formal way, at a young and younger age, may be strong for nursery and playgroup providers who are concerned that they are seen to be preparing children to fit in with the start of formal National Curriculum work. They may have concerns that their funding providers will be looking for evidence of written work, particularly work relating to counting, shape recognition and number formation. Television and newspaper reports about falling levels of numeracy in our schools, and the need to improve the situation, can be misunderstood and pressure from parents to do formal work at a younger age may be strong.

A minority of children are ready to do this type of written work in a more formal way. They enjoy it, understand it and learn from it. They have the prerequisite skills in place. Others – the great majority – are just not ready. They need much more time to play with all the concepts that form the basic building blocks of mathematics. They need much more time for physical play to understand space, shape and measurement. They need time to make sense of counting and to use it naturally as part of their play because it delights them and they can see a real use for it. They need enough time to explore their world so that their thinking skills, their curiosity and their longing to solve problems are really ready before tackling more formal maths. Over-emphasis on formality too soon may even be damaging.

Early years service providers are in a ideal position to hold back from formal written work. All the mathematics that can be done on paper, for pre-school and Reception-age children, can also be done mentally using equipment, objects and visual aids. Counting the biscuits on the plate and working out whether there will be enough for you and your friends is much more interesting than filling in the answer to how many dots there are on a worksheet. It is more relevant too, as each person takes a biscuit there is one less on a plate. It is much more satisfying to work out the new totals of biscuits as they are taken away than by doing pages of abstract written sums where you have to subtract 1 each time. Mathematically able young children can also enjoy practical applications even if the arithmetic involved is easy.

However if they need to, early years providers can demonstrate evidence of providing mathematical learning opportunities in many ways, for example by:

- staff keeping notes of learning to add to children's individual records of achievement
- showing termly, weekly and daily plans of activities
- giving details of staff training and external courses attended
- listing relevant equipment and books that satisfy different areas of mathematical learning
- displaying artwork and models produced by children (or photographic records of this work – this resolves storage problems with bulky quantities of artwork)
- keeping a photographic record of displays relating to maths
- showing photographs of activities containing a mathematical content actually taking place, linked to descriptions of the activities by the staff involved
- using noticeboards to give useful ideas for parents and carers to take up at home

- drawing from previous OFSTED inspections and inspection reports of teaching or other early years work in action.

Worksheets do not have to feature in a significant way, or at all. Some children may be fascinated by written representations of numbers and calculations and of course their written work is relevant too, but it does not have to be the focus for all children.

Children who refuse to engage in mathematical activities in early years settings may be doing so because they are being expected to do too much abstract or written work too soon. It may also be because they have general or specific mathematical abilities or skills that are not being met.

Summary

- There is a concern that the introduction of the National Curriculum is having an impact on early years teaching. Some nurseries, playgroups and parents are now expecting children to do more formal work at a much younger age.
- Most children under school age are not ready for formal, written maths – they need to learn through play and practical examples and to use their mathematical learning in play.
- Early years providers can demonstrate in many ways evidence of providing mathematical learning opportunities apart from showing children's written work.

Able children

Any discussion on able children immediately throws up the problem of how you identify them. This is especially problematic in early years teaching yet is critical that they are recognised as soon as possible so that they can receive an appropriate programme of education and don't settle into the rut of underachievement.

Sometimes we have pre-conceptions of what an able-child is like – well motivated and hard-working with neat presentation of work and effective use of language – but none of these are relevant criteria in assessing ability. Able children who lack confidence, or fail to participate actively in class because of boredom, can easily be overlooked. The restless child who seems unable to concentrate on simple maths work could have considerable potential waiting to be unlocked but if they are never challenged at a higher level they will never have the chance to shine.

It would be so simple if we could just devise a test to sort out those with high maths ability. Indeed, various IQ tests are sometimes used but the results are on the whole unreliable in that they fail to measure many subtle and important aspects of the character and abilities of the really able child. Indeed, at primary school level it is sensitive teaching staff who have the greatest success in recognising a child with special talents.

Mathematically able children can sometimes be identified as young as four or five years old. They often share with older children some of these identifiable characteristics:

- recognition of the structure in patterns
- fascination with numbers and their application
- confidence in manipulating numbers
- an ability to develop their own strategies for solving maths problems where they haven't yet been taught an appropriate method
- delight in learning about, and working with, big numbers

A child's mathematical ability can show up in all sorts of ways and is not limited to solving long 'sums' correctly. Able children's thinking may extend beyond the maths of numbers and be quite philosophical in nature or concerned with applications directly connected to the world around them. They may show academic ability right across the curriculum or their interests and talents may be focused in just one or two areas. Supporting children who are identified as having a higher level of mathematical ability can prove challenging but there are ways to extend and enrich their experience of maths.

Large numbers – thinking big

A common interest that many mathematically able children have is in large numbers. This can be confusing for childcare workers who are used to working with numbers up to ten, or maybe twenty. Many of the resources, equipment, books, songs and rhymes available are geared towards that number range. The National Curriculum is structured so that younger children are expected to work mostly with smaller numbers. The magnitude of numbers gradually increases so that, by the middle of Key Stage 2, children will be familiar with thousands, tens of thousands and beyond. So what can you do with a young child who is fascinated by large numbers and is feeling bored or limited by the idea of smaller ones?

Answering their questions about 'what comes next?' in number sequences is important. If you don't know yourself, say so and find out. (Acknowledging that you may have to look in a book or ask someone to find out something you don't know is a wonderful example to any child – you are demonstrating research skills.) If the child wants to think bigger and bigger don't feel afraid of talking about the idea of infinity – when the number sequence becomes so large that it extends for ever into a concept that can no longer be called a number. Young, mathematically able children often revel in this kind of idea.

Making collections of things is one way to go bigger. Collecting autumn leaves does not need to stop at ten or twenty, or even a hundred, if you have the time and patience to continue. You can look at the trees and estimate how many leaves are left, or kick through the drifts of leaves on the ground and guess how many have fallen off. The maths is still physical and exploratory but is at the intellectual level that the child needs. Many things in the natural world lend themselves to counting or estimating in large numbers, e.g. blades of grass, grains of sand, blackberries in the hedgerow. Taking apart a ripe sunflower head and guessing at the number of seeds, then extracting and counting them all, is fascinating especially if you take a good look at the spiral patterns in which the seeds are arranged. Try estimating what might be a big number, a huge number or an absolutely gigantic number (think of hairs on your head, grass in the playground, grains of sugar in the packet, stars in the sky).

There are several superb books for this age range in the *Wonderwise* series published by Watts. Some of the most useful ones start with something that the child knows and understands and then extends out into the world, introducing masses of ideas. *What's Under the Bed?* and *What's Up?* by Mick Manning and Brita Granstrom look at what exists between us and the centre of the earth or us and the far reaches of outer space respectively. Thinking huge is part of their content. *Is a Blue Whale the Biggest Thing There is?* by Robert E. Wells is about, to quote the introduction, 'the UNIVERSE, and other Very Big Things. So it uses Very Big Numbers – even MILLIONS and BILLIONS.' Producing a book for younger children that makes sense of the size of the universe would seem impossible but this book has done it and it's a delightful resource for children longing to discover more about this subject.

BEAM produce a book in their *Starting From Mathematical Ideas* series called *Big Numbers*. Although much of its contents is geared to older children, some of the ideas for things to do would be appropriate for work with older able children in nursery settings.

Large numbers – writing big

Sometimes children are naturally curious about writing numbers that have a bigger value. The example shown was produced during free-play in nursery by a child of four years three months. He had learnt to write the numbers up to 10 and, having been told by his mother at home how to write 100, worked out independently how to write in hundreds up to 900. He got stuck at 1000 and decided to stop. If he had been interested in continuing it would have been entirely appropriate for a member to staff to have helped him to write 1000, then again allow him to work out where to go from there.

The child may or may not have been able to count up to this amount. He may or may not have understood the idea of **place value** (*hundreds, tens, units* etc.) or had a mental picture of what these large numbers would have looked like in terms of objects but he was identifying, in a logical way, the pattern that our number system follows.

So, if the child wants it, don't restrict your counting, estimating or looking

A four-year-old writing in hundreds.

at written representations to the numbers from 0 to 10. Don't be afraid to go bigger if appropriate.

Co-ordination, visual and spatial skills

Some children show strong abilities in visual or spatial skills and these are often, although not always, linked to good co-ordination.

Spatial skills: people doing cartwheels drawn without moving the paper.

The drawing of two figures was produced by a child with these kinds of abilities at two years eleven months of age. The figures contain a lot of detail for a child of this age. The interesting thing that he did in his drawing, however, was to draw the second figure, *without moving the paper*, as an upside-down version of the first. He put in all the details in the correct relation to each other but upside-down. He was tremendously excited about discovering he could do this and called his pictures of this type 'people doing cartwheels'. The spatial awareness needed to draw one drawing and then to redraw it rotated in this way is very interesting.

Children who display these early signs of spatial ability can be supported by providing them with the means to make and build using construction toys and educational materials as well as junk modelling or wordwork. They can be encouraged to plan their work mentally before they proceed with it, to draw their ideas before and after construction, and to evaluate their work aloud. Look together at the instructions for using construction toys. They

Constructing the framework of a play tent from canes.

may be fascinated by pictorial instructions. Don't throw out these sorts of leaflets or backs-of-packets – share them.

Young children with good spatial ability may well enjoy pattern making, including experimentation with rotation and reflection of images. They will probably be able to do much more complicated jigsaws than average. Their drawing, including very careful observational drawing, can be encouraged too.

The publishers *Tarquin* (see Appendix 3) produce materials that can be used as extension work for more able children of all ages. Their puzzle packs on tangrams and pentominoes may prove very successful for this age group. They also produce some fascinating materials relating to the exploration of reflections and symmetry. *Binary Arts* (see Appendix 3) manufacture puzzles that are sold in high-street shops and that have proved very successful with children with well-developed spatial awareness.

The children in the photograph had decided how they wanted to construct the framework of a tent out of canes and were being helped to follow their

Copying the tent design in miniature for play people.

design. They covered the framework with large pieces of cloth and played together in and around the tent for an hour or so. When the girl (four years six months) came indoors to play she made a small-scale replica of the garden tent out of lolly sticks and paper for her play people completely on her own. She used her strong sense of the three dimensional form and her well-developed fine motor skills to make it so accurately that it stood up and fitted the play people beautifully.

At no time did she talk about having made a **triangular prism** (the mathematical name for the framework) and it would not have been appropriate to interrupt her play at the time to give her that description. However, we are sure that when she starts to name and explore the geometry of solids in more formal maths her understanding and ability to visualise the three-dimensional form will make it very easy. She knows how these solids fit together and her abilities are being resourced in such a way that she is able to create her own enrichment activities.

Summary

- Mathematically able children may show academic ability right across the curriculum or their interests and talents may be focused in just one or two areas.
- Mathematical ability may show up in all sorts of ways:
  - in calculation and a creative ability in manipulating numbers
  - philosophically
  - in practical applications
  - in visual and spatial skills.

Specific learning disabilities

There are many different conditions that can affect the learning of maths. Dyslexia, dyspraxia and discalcula are some that have been identified. They can be further complicated because each condition presents itself in a variety of ways. No two children are identical. Moreover, possession of a specific condition might go along with high academic ability, or it may go alongside a cocktail of other conditions that hinder a child's learning.

Some people believe that such problems are not connected with the child's ability to learn but with the adult's ability to teach in a way that enables a child to learn, so that maybe these kinds of conditions should be thought of as 'teaching difficulties'.

Children who show signs of difficulties with maths need to be assessed independently so that their specific needs are addressed. This will probably happen during Key Stage 1 if children are showing visible signs of struggling with aspects of their learning. However, we have both worked with children whose difficulties in learning maths have only been noticed later in primary school. The sooner difficulties are identified the better, as long as appropriate help can then be provided for the children, geared to their specific needs.

Very often, one of the problems that arises is when a child has been directed into more formal learning too soon and fear of failure and of being seen to be stupid becomes a kind of self-fulfilling prophecy. Again, we have both worked with children who are terrified of making mistakes mathematically. The focus, through the National Numeracy Strategy, on whole-class teaching in mathematics seems daunting to these children especially where staff choose to teach mental arithmetic in a way that puts a child 'on the spot' in front of his or her friends. There are strengths and weaknesses in all different teaching methods, and whole-class sessions need to be managed in a very sensitive way if there are some in the group who are struggling and scared. For instance, teachers can invite responses to questions rather than randomly picking on individual children to answer questions fired at them.

Very often the sorts of multi-sensory, play-based activities followed by pre-school children with a tendency to dyslexia, dyspraxia or discalcula are exactly the sorts of activities that will help them with maths when they are older. Giving children a good start with these, in a way that makes them feel confident and successful in the early years, will help them in overcoming difficulties later.

Dyslexia

Dyslexia is a learning disability that specifically relates to reading, spelling and written language. Dyslexics may not have trouble with maths but many do. Learning mathematical ideas, vocabulary, numbers and symbols can be as hard as learning to manage the written word. Following sequences or recognising patterns can prove very difficult. Short-term memory may be affected. The child may not process spoken instructions comprehensively, especially those given quickly. Some children talk about words on the page moving around or dancing, and they may find a larger quantity of writing on a page too much to cope with.

If an older child with dyslexia has managed to overcome, or is not affected by, problems with maths but has difficulties reading text or writing, their ability to show their mathematical competence will be affected. Reading instructions for problems and writing full answers may be difficulties that get in the way even if the child can cope with the mathematical content of the work itself. It is important that, if there are reading difficulties, tailor-made help is given to overcome these alongside any mathematical learning problems.

There seem to be many ways of thinking, remembering and learning about things: some of us like hands-on experiments; others prefer pictures or two-dimensional drawings; some of us learning in a sequential way – one thing logically leading on from another; others have apparently unlinked flashes of understanding. Early years professionals and parents wanting to support children with specific learning difficulties need to offer help in different ways while they find out how those children learn best.

In early years settings, where most children will not be expected to be reading, writing or doing maths on paper, the early signs of dyslexia may not be immediately noticeable. First attempts by all children learning to write numbers and letters often show reversal of character shapes. The previous example of numbers written in the hundreds by a four-year-old (see 'Large numbers – writing big') shows many numbers reversed. However, in this example, the child does show the ability to deduce and logically order the sequences of characters – an activity that young dyslexics can find difficult.

This particular child's spatial skills are strong (a situation that is found in many people with dyslexia) and he also comes from a family where close relations have been diagnosed as dyslexic. Having close family members who have reading difficulties (or formally diagnosed dyslexia) may indicate potential dyslexic tendencies in the child. There seems to be an inherited component in some cases.

In an early years setting dyslexic children might be helped by:

- high-quality observation and development of the ways in which learning seems to be successful and applications of these methods to all different areas of learning
- aiming to provide multi-sensory play for all activities where possible
- helping a child to recall and recognise sequences, or recognise patterns;

practising numbers sequences in a wide variety of ways (with songs, jumps, hands-on counting of everything, pouring cupfuls of water or shovelling sand out of the sandpit – make it as multi-sensory as possible)
- encouraging regular practice in using short-term memory (e.g. playing simple memory games, remembering words to songs, rhymes or books or asking a child to take a simple message to another member of staff)
- dealing with instructions one at a time – perhaps removing or covering up equipment and instructions that are not being used for that particular task
- speaking clearly and slowly; not rushing instructions; double-checking understanding
- keeping good records of observations and findings to pass on to future educators – information about ways of learning that do and don't work may prove extremely useful to new teachers.

Maths for the Dyslexic by Anne Henderson is a useful resource for those who want to continue looking at how the needs of older school-age children can be met.

Dyscalcula

A person affected by dyscalcula has difficulties with calculating. They may be unable to recognise number symbols and maintain the order of numbers when counting. When such a child encounters arithmetic they may make many small errors, swap numbers over in transcription, and lose track of what they are doing: was it adding or subtracting? They may also find it difficult to cope with sequences, to be aware of the time and to apply ideas understood in one question when answering a similar one elsewhere. They may be good readers and writers and so everyone may think they are lazy or just need to concentrate more on their maths. They may find coping with the maths they encounter in the real world extremely hard: shopping, timekeeping and daily organisation may provide particularly challenging. In younger children difficulties in reading and writing numbers and in managing sequences may be the first signs of difficulty.

Awareness of dyscalcula is not as widespread as that of dyslexia. Diagnosis and procedures for helping people cope with this condition may not be so widely available. Strategies suggested for supporting children with possible dyslexic tendencies would seem to be applicable here as well, especially those to do with sequencing, concentration and multi-sensory approaches to reading and writing number shapes. As with dyslexia it may help to experiment with drawing and making numbers in many multi-sensory ways: in sand, food, paint, mud, or with water squirted from a washing-up liquid bottle onto dry paving slabs. Make numbers with finger shapes, using your whole body, in a collage, with string or sown in cress seeds. Make numbers huge and tiny. Trace them on steamy window panes. Run along the shapes of numbers marked on the ground in the outdoor play area.

Having dyslexia or dyscalcula does not reflect a person's intelligence. In private correspondence, the mother of a dyslexic girl wrote to us with this very clear view on the conditions:

'There would seem to be plenty of evidence that Einstein was dyslexic. Also he could not speak until he was five and his was dyscalculaic all his life, to the extent that he was fired twice from positions teaching maths because he couldn't do arithmetic. But, as is the case with all the dyslexics I know, his brain worked so fast and so completely in three-dimensions that the theory of relativity came to him in its entirety, as a daydream (pejorative term used about most dyslexics!) which he then sorted out into terms he could explain to others.

Dyslexia did cause Einstein trouble at school but it also gave him great brilliance. Dyslexics aren't given talents to compensate for their difficulties; if anything it is more that the difficulties are a cross they have to bear as a result of having the greater gifts, and it doesn't have to happen. It is a teaching, not a learning disability and if individual thinking is valued over rote learning it doesn't happen at all.'

Dyspraxia

This describes a condition where a child has difficulty in planning and carrying out complex movements. A child will find it difficult to demonstrate the sort of co-ordinated activity that is in keeping with their chronological age and intelligence. Although some children with dyspraxia may have other difficulties, such as reading or speech problems, many show no other signs of difficulty.

Children with dyspraxia may experiences delays in being able to walk, run or jump. They may fall or trip a lot and they may show poor gross motor skills when playing on large items of equipment. They may find fine motor skills difficult: detailed drawing or the finer details of dressing may be hard to accomplish. There concentration and their short-term memory, both visual and verbal, may be poor.

This may affect mathematical learning in the early years in many ways. Difficulties in running, jumping, balancing and climbing may affect the child's understanding of words that relate to shape, space, distance and speed. Lack of fine motor skills may affect the ability to do puzzles, play board games, engage in more sophisticated role-play and count small objects. Poor memory and concentration might affect a lot of different areas of learning.

Unlike dyslexia and dyscalcula, dyspraxia may be identified more easily in pre-school children. The difference in a child's behaviour in relation to their peers may have been picked up by parents and carers or at health-checks. A physiotherapy assessment may have been made before a child reaches school-age or before the end of Key Stage 1. Concrete suggestions for practice to improve co-ordination and memory may be being used in education and home settings, by occupational therapists and physiotherapists, teaching staff and parents. A co-ordinated treatment plan with regular reviews may continue long term for children substantially affected by dyspraxia. Other children are only mildly affected and their difficulties may resolve themselves much more quickly.

Summary

- There are many different conditions that can affect the learning of maths including dyslexia, dyscalcula and dyspraxia. Each condition can present itself in a variety of ways.
- Each child showing signs of difficulties with maths needs to be assessed independently so that his or her specific needs are addressed.
- Giving children a good start with multi-sensory, play-based activities in the early years so that they feel confident and successful will help them in overcoming potential difficulties in later years.
- Having dyslexia, dyscalcula or dyspraxia does not reflect on a person's intelligence.

Left-handedness

Nobody would think of left-handedness as a disability nowadays and naturally left-handed children will not be forced to learn to write with their right hands any more. However, in mathematics there are some items of equipment we use that are designed for a right-handed user and it can be difficult for a left-handed person to use this sort of equipment.

It is important that scissors are available which a left-handed child can use in construction and design work. Left-handed scissors are available through some of the larger high-street stationers or educational suppliers. Left-handed rulers (where the numbering system starts from 0 on the right hand side) are also available from specialist suppliers (see Appendix 3) although there are mixed feelings about the necessity for these. You might also make sure that there is enough space around a computer in the classroom for the mouse to be used on either side of the keyboard. If a child has dedicated use of a computer, e.g. at home, then it is possible to have the mouse permanently adjusted so that the left and right-click functions are reversed. A school might also consider having a spare left-hand adjusted mouse to plug in where needed on a machine regularly used by a left-handed child (or member of staff).

Hearing and visual impairment

Hearing impaired children

Hearing impairment may occur for a variety of reasons; substantial hearing loss will be more obvious but gradual or temporary hearing loss can be harder to identify. Any child suspected of having difficulties with their hearing needs to see the appropriate professionals for diagnostic hearing tests.

In helping a child engaged in early years maths activities, make sure that they can see your face really clearly throughout the session, that they are ready to begin at the start and that background noise is reduced. Ensure your introduction to activities, and your speaking, is very clear. Summarise what you have done at the end.

Many early years maths activities are hands-on and visual; a fully sighted, hearing impaired child may need careful reinforcement of mathematical words but at least they will have a visual picture of what they are trying to learn.

Visually impaired children

Learning mathematics can be very much more complicated for a child who finds it difficult to see. Specialist help will be necessary for a child who is blind. However, children who are seriously short- or long-sighted can be helped more easily. Sit the child in the group where they have the clearest views of books being read or equipment demonstrated. Acquire equipment that is larger in size: giant pegboards and pegs, giant dice or dominoes. If it helps the child, use selections of equipment that have the clearest contrasting colours. Experiment with lighting in the room. Use big book versions when reading where possible. Large-character computer keyboards can be made available for older children. (Computers can help children with learning difficulties in all kinds of ways as they get older. Dyslexic children can sometimes cope with reading and writing text using a computer when the handwritten word would be very difficult for them.)

Much early years mathematical equipment is designed in bright colours. Early mathematical activities that encourage sorting, colouring, copying or building often involve manipulating items in different colours. If a child manages to cope with other maths activities but struggles with colour it may be that they are just too young to manage the activity: it is common for young children to confuse shape and colour as concepts. It may also be that they are colour blind. It is said that five to ten per cent of all males have impaired colour vision, so one can assume that a similar proportion of young boys are also affected. A much smaller proportion of girls have impaired colour vision.

If you are concerned about a child's colour vision, consult colleagues and discuss your observations with the child's parents so that they can request assessment if necessary. Take care that sorting activities are conducted with different criteria for sorting, e.g. by patterns, or use strongly contrasting coloured pieces, e.g. dark blue and white. Until you are sure that children understand the ideas of shape or colour as separate concepts, try not to use sorting activities that mix the two. Make sequences using 'triangle, circle, square' repeated in one colour only, or sort identically shaped buttons into 'red-blue-blue' repeating patterns. Be sure that the child understands what the variables are that you are using to produce a sequence before trying a 'red triangle, blue triangle, red square, blue square' sequence for example. Otherwise it gets too confusing.

There are common suggestions for support of any child facing difficulties or challenges in their abilities to learn.

- It is important for any child, particularly any child with learning-related difficulties, to preserve a strong sense of self-worth. All children need positive feedback and need to be valued for who they are and what they can contribute, rather than criticised for what they cannot do.
- Children need to learn the things they find difficult in an

environment where they are able to concentrate well, maybe by sitting closer to the adult helping them if working in a large group or by keeping the group size small or working one-to-one.

- Try to keep amounts of information in instructions concise.
- Sub-divide difficulties into smaller, more manageable parts that can be tackled methodically.
- Help children create their own strategies for solving their own difficulties.
- Ensure good liaison between all professionals, parents and carers involved with helping the child and seek specialist help where appropriate.

Sand and water

This picture reminds us, once again, of the value of free-play in the sandpit. These children were engaged in a very co-operative game involving digging a big hole and filling it with water. The children were organising who would dig a specified number of spadefuls and who would collect another bucket of water. The child who collected the water discovered again and again what constituted a *full* bucket and felt the difference in weights between a full and an empty one. The children were taking turns

There are many opportunities for mathematical learning in the sandpit.

sorting out who went *first*, *second* and so on. They were sharing the play but they were also engaged in the activity at the physical and intellectual level they each needed on that day.

None of the children here had been diagnosed as having 'special educational needs' but their learning needs would have differed anyway simply because all children are different from each other. A child fascinated by maths might be wondering if it would take a hundred buckets of water to fill the whole sandpit. A child finding it hard to concentrate that day may be feeling very pleased with the hole they had just dug. A child wanting to tackle a tricky piece of co-ordinated activity might want to be the person filling the bucket, working out when it was full and trying to carry it to the sandpit without spilling any. A child who is a natural leader may be adopting that role in the group, while another who is a brilliant problem solver may be sorting out an argument about who should use the biggest spade next. Differentiated learning happens quite naturally in a situation like this and, on a good day, all the children's needs are catered for. Childcare professionals need to observe and support if necessary, maybe by suggesting an idea that would extend a project, or maybe later by following up an investigation or question indoors with other equipment. Multi-sensory play (particularly the muddy, sandy, wet sort) has many benefits for all children.

> ## *Summary*
> - Make sure that the needs of left-handed children are catered for, especially by providing appropriate scissors.
> - Adapt the environment and provide appropriate equipment so that hearing impaired or visually impaired children benefit from the mathematical activities available.
> - All children's learning needs differ from day to day depending on their moods, current interests, energy levels and so on.
> - Multi-sensory play has benefits for all children.

Watching out for words

Mathematical words tend to be very precise and, even in an early years setting, some words can become problematic. It is useful to be aware that there can be problems. A few examples are discussed here.

Words such as 'on' in English are used in a variety of ways and this can take some time to decode. We switch the television *on*. We put shoes *on*. We put a cup *on* the table. We put the dinner *on*. All have different meanings. The mathematical use of the word, where *on* means 'on top of' may be one of the easiest uses to decipher.

'Big' can be more confusing. It used to mean 'tall', 'generally large', 'older' (as in 'big sister'), 'fat', 'wide', 'heavy' and so on. Use the more precise word where possible and ask children to qualify their use of *big*. What kind of *big*? Sometimes *big* (older) sisters or brothers are not physically *big* and if this confusion can be avoided, try to do so.

Try also to avoid expressions such as 'a *few* more than ...' or '*lots* less than ...'. They can be very confusing to a three-year-old trying to make sense of all these comparative words. How can something be *few* and *more*, or *lots* and *less*, at the same time?

Comparisons relating to size may also be very confusing and an adult's explanation is very helpful. The example that is often cited is that of a big mouse being much smaller than an elephant. Drawing pictures, roughly to scale, helps a child understand that mice come in a range of sizes and so do elephants. Big and small, in these examples, relate to these ranges.

If you find that children are getting confused with any mathematical words, stay aware that this could be arising because of ambiguity in the use or choice of vocabulary.

Adults' attitudes to numeracy

Some parents had good experiences in learning maths in school and are confident about helping their children with early maths. However, there are many parents who are not so confident or who are quite happy to talk, in front of their children, about how difficult maths is and how much they hate it.

If we want children to grow up confident in maths we need to watch how we talk about it. Sometimes girls hear the adult women around them saying negative things about maths, and this is one role model they can do without.

Nurseries, playgroups and childminders can play a useful role in encouraging parents to feel confident about supporting their children's learning. Maybe a nursery could run a session for parents demonstrating many of the ways that they enable mathematical learning to happen in the nursery. Maybe a playgroup could add many more resources relating to maths to the lending sections of their library,. Walker books (see Appendix 3) have produced *Maths Together* packs with six story and puzzle books in each, for 3+ and 5+ year-olds. The books have a specifically mathematical content and contain parents' notes with ideas for use with children, providing an excellent addition to library shelves. Some playgroups have created 'story bags' with books and related toy(s) in bags that can be borrowed from their library. The books and toys might be on a mathematical theme: a book telling the traditional tale of *The Three Billy Goats Gruff* accompanied by three toy goats of differing sizes, a toy 'troll' and a few bricks to build a bridge, for example. Likewise some groups lend puzzles and simple mathematical games on a library system.

The Basic Skills Agency have produced a pack on supporting young children's maths called *Count and figure it out together*, containing masses of ideas of things to do with pre-school and younger school-aged children. Maths Year 2000, like the National Year of Literacy the year before, has generated many more materials for parents. Some further education colleges run courses for parents who want to help their children's learning. Parents who want to improve their own skills in numeracy (and literacy too) can be given information about the Basic Skills Agency which runs courses for adults.

Presenting parents with ideas for mathematical things to do with their children which do not involve pen and paper sums is really important. The high-street shops are now full of early maths workbooks geared towards pre-schoolers and many parents buy these to 'help' their children to learn. Even if children enjoy this sort of thing, do encourage parents to *play* mathematically too.

Many early years professionals are nervous about the mathematical content of their work. In order not to transmit this fear to the children in their care, it is important to deal with the worries. Colleagues may be supportive or there may be in-service courses to enable staff to feel more confident in maths. Many of the resources for parents will encourage confidence. It may help to borrow equipment from the playgroup or nursery for the weekend and take it home to play with and think about the mathematical potential of the items. If you were not lucky enough to 'play mathematics' as a child, you can catch up now. The Pre-School Learning Alliance have produced a very useful booklet *What do we mean by maths?* that explains, in more detail, subject knowledge relevant to early years mathematical learning. If you don't understand words you encounter in your professional reading on learning about numbers, volume and capacity, weight and mass or shapes, particularly solids, take a look at this booklet. The fact that you are nervous about mathematics yourself is not to do with your own abilities, it is almost certainly connected with your having had the wrong kind of teaching and learning experiences when you were young.

As we said earlier, it is fine to admit to your own lack of knowledge. Share your search for answers with the children in your care, learn afresh alongside them and remember to stay positive about maths for their sakes.

Summary

- Some mathematical words have non-mathematical or ambiguous meanings. We need to stay aware that confusion can arise from imprecise use.
- We need to ensure that children hear us talk positively about maths if we are to be good role models.
- Nurseries, playgroups and childminders can play a useful role in encouraging parents to feel confident about supporting their children's learning.
- Parents, teaching staff and carers who want to become more confident in their own mathematical abilities can find many materials and courses to help them.

5

Beginning Maths at School

Children entering primary, infant or first school bring with them very different experiences of learning and a correspondingly diverse range of skills and knowledge. In order to get a clear picture of each child's abilities, the government has introduced a statutory requirement for every child in the state system to be assessed. For further details see Appendix 2.

Many children entering the school system will have attended at least half-days at nursery school or playgroup where learning primarily evolved from play activities. Others will have spent their days with a childminder, nanny or parent where the carer will have had a more dominant role in the development of the child. Both these groups of children present the teaching staff of a Reception class with the same challenge: to ensure the happy transition from the less formal, play-oriented, pre-school experience to the more structured format of classroom teaching. It should be a gentle, happy transition with familiar elements of playgroup or nursery school still retained.

The content of maths teaching in schools is specified in the National Curriculum. Until recently the method of teaching that syllabus was left to individual schools but in September 1999 the government introduced the National Numeracy Strategy which contained recommendations on content and structure for a 'daily maths lesson'. Although not statutory, most state schools in England now follow the guidelines and practice laid down in the National Numeracy Strategy's *Framework for teaching mathematics from Reception to Year 6* and have introduced a daily maths lesson of between 45 minutes and one hour. This has become popularly known as the 'Numeracy Hour', a partner to the earlier-established Literacy Hour.

This chapter looks at ways to help teaching staff involved with Reception and Year 1 to build mathematical confidence in their pupils both within and beyond the designated maths lesson. Many of our suggestions may not seem to correlate directly to the Numeracy Strategy but they are designed to extend and support the material in it. The chapter consists of four main sections which correspond to the four strands specified for Reception and Year 1 in the Framework of the National Numeracy Strategy. These are: numbers and the number system; calculations, solving problems; measures, shape and space. Inevitably there is considerable overlap in many of the activities under the different headings. Indeed this is highly desirable as it is helpful for children to meet the same ideas in different contexts. It is through the continuing process of repetition, reinforcement and extension that mathematical ideas become a natural part of a child's thinking.

Numbers and the number system

This section covers the vocabulary and understanding of basic number skills. It has been divided into six sub-sections which cover some of the main themes met in Reception and Year 1:

- counting from one to ten
- counting to more than ten
- number lines and number squares
- using numbers
- why count?
- guessing
- reading and writing numerals.

Counting from one to ten

We have stressed in this book the importance of counting with small children at every opportunity. Of course many of the children in Reception will not have had such extensive exposure to the experience of counting but some will be able to demonstrate fluent counting of numbers in their correct order up to or beyond ten. This does not necessarily mean they have any understanding of the way numbers are used.

Young children can count a row of objects, recount the same number of objects several times and not be at all bothered if they get a different final number at each counting. Even if they count more reliably and always end up with the same number, they might not have understood the significance of the last number.

Here is an exchange between a teacher and Tom who is just five years old:

Teacher [*with a row of six bricks*]: Can you count these?
Tom: Yes ... [*touching each brick*] 1, 2, 3, 4, 5, 6.
Teacher: So how many are there?

> *Tom: [counting again, very carefully]*: 1, 2, 3, 4, 5, 6.
> *Teacher*: So there are six, are there?
> [*Tom goes very quiet.*]
> *Teacher [putting the six bricks in a pile]*: I've got six bricks . . . [*pushing them over to Tom*]: How many have you got?
> *Tom [counting again, carefully touching each brick]*: 1, 2, 3, 4, 5, 6.

Do you think Tom understands that the last number he says in the counting sequence is the actual total? Or perhaps he thinks counting is giving each brick a name, a number name?

This example does not mean that rote learning of the correct number sequence is unimportant or trivial − far from it. Research has shown that children with a good list of rote-learned numbers are also capable of a whole range of other number tasks. Reciting number names in the correct order is the framework underlying the whole structure of maths.

Let's take a closer look at the skill of counting. Clearly a great deal of practice is needed before a long list of number words can be said in the correct order but endless reciting can be boring, and it doesn't show the underlying patterns in the number sequence. In nursery school, number rhymes and songs were learnt to help with memorising number order. These can still be used and extended with props, especially number cards.

ACTIVITY

A simple song, such a *One, two, three, four, five − once I caught a fish alive* . . ., can be extended and enlivened by giving each of ten children a card with a number from 1 to 10 on it. When their number is called the child jumps up. Many other nursery songs can be used with children holding number cards. The following songs encourage counting backwards from five: *Five Little Ducks*, *Five Currant Buns*, and *Five Fat Sausages*. For counting backwards from ten, the song *Ten Green Bottles* can be used and extended to higher numbers whenever required (*This Little Puffin* is a good source for this type of song). All these activities clearly have a much richer mathematical content than just counting forwards and backwards. They introduce basic ideas of addition and subtraction. They also encourage children to become familiar with the symbols representing each number.

Whole class teaching in the daily maths lesson.

Many resources have been developed to support whole-class teaching for the daily maths lesson. The 'bananas' in the picture are used for displaying answers to the teacher's questions. Given that there is a wide range of this type of material to choose from, it is worth spending time researching the options so that you can select the most appropriate for your classroom.

Counting is, of course, only learnt through constant repetition. It is therefore important to keep the counting experience fresh and fun, otherwise many children will begin to switch off as soon as they hear the first few familiar numbers. To inject some humour into counting, some teachers introduce a puppet along the lines of 'The Count' in *Sesame Street*. It can encourage a great deal of child participation, especially if your puppet doesn't seem to count very well and relies on the children to correct him! The puppet can miss out numbers when counting and give incorrect answers when challenged to say 'the next number' on 'the number before . . .' or 'the number after . . .'. The puppet's answers, whispered in the teacher's ear, can be absurd – a totally ridiculous number like 'a million' or 'lemons'. Having an argumentative puppet not only increases the fun but can help to explore all sorts of mathematical ideas. For example: a puppet that announces that twenty is after the number nine could insist that, since twenty is bigger than nine, it does come after it and then point this out on the number line. The teacher then has the opportunity to explain very patiently to the irate puppet exactly what is meant by 'after' in her question. The puppet can also write on the board, select number cards, point on the number square and be part of a whole puppet family of mathematical incompetents with perhaps one maths professor who always gets everything right.

There is a tremendous range of objects to count in the classroom but, when counting from one to ten, sometimes the most obvious set of objects can be overlooked – FINGERS! They are invaluable in early years maths and give us the basic understanding of working with a decimal number-system. They make numbers part of us and teach us **number bonds** to ten (pairs of numbers that add up to ten) very easily. Most importantly, they are a portable calculator that is with us wherever we go!

Fingers are tremendously useful in early years maths.

Counting to more than ten

Children need not be confined to counting from one to ten until they are totally proficient. It is important that they be exposed to larger numbers in order to learn the patterns of the number sequence. Unfortunately, in English there are a whole lot of new words to learn as soon as we go above ten. Furthermore, these words don't clearly show how they are related to ten. It would be much easier if eleven were called 'ten-one', twelve 'ten-two' etc. It can be very valuable to point out to children how unusual the names of the numbers are. It has been found that children learn the significance of a number more quickly if you ask them what they think it should be called and then say 'but we call it twelve'.

There can also be discussion about the words for 'two tens', 'three tens', 'four tens' and so on. Try and get the children to recognise the word-pattern of these numbers. Try to stress the 'tee' sound at the end of twen**ty**, thir**ty**, for**ty** etc. 'Twenty' and 'thirty' are of course not clearly sound related to 'two tens' and 'three tens', but once you get to 'forty' the sound link with 'four' can be pointed out. Even 'fifty' sounds rather like 'five-tee'. 'Sixty', 'seventy', 'eighty' and 'ninety' are the easy ones. Recognising the sound pattern makes counting in tens relatively easy to achieve.

There are many ways to encourage a corresponding development in the mathematical understanding of counting in tens. One suggestion is given below.

ACTIVITY

Take ten large, empty egg boxes that usually hold a dozen eggs. Cut them down so that each only holds ten eggs. Get the children to make ten 'eggs' out of modelling material. Label each box clearly with a number '10'. As you count in tens, pile the boxes on top of each other. Remove the boxes as you count backwards. This could occasionally be done with more than ten boxes so that, for example, two hundred is reached.

Number lines and number squares

When teaching counting, especially above the number ten, number lines and number squares are helpful. They enable children to begin to learn the numerical symbols for each number. They provide the teacher with lots of opportunity to discuss patterns in the number sequence and can also be the centre of many number games and puzzles.

Number lines can take many different forms. They can be arranged as a ladder climbing the way or hung on a 'washing line' strung along a wall. Large floor tiles with numbers drawn on them can be laid out on the floor for number jumping-games – laying the tiles in the correct order is a game in itself.

A number square to a hundred can be introduced at a very early stage to show the patterns in the higher numbers. Some of the most useful squares will have removable numbers. These might be plastic sheets with pockets or magnetic boards. Try covering or removing a number in the number square and then challenge the children to work out what is missing. Swap a couple of numbers and see if any of the children can spot them. Of course you don't have to use the whole hundred number square for any of these activities but children who are not yet counting reliably to twenty still enjoy spotting the patterns in numbers to a hundred. It is helpful to point out how all the numbers ending in '1' line up in a 'column'. On other days look at different 'columns' or identify 'rows' and talk about the digit that remains the same.

Counting in twos

A separate number chart may be used to demonstrate counting in twos. The pairs of numbers can be lined up in a column. The numbers can be drawn so that they are each shown with a pair of arms. They can then be shown holding hands, so that it is clear that they are arranged in pairs. The class will probably already have the experience of 'finding a partner' or 'standing in pairs' in line to go to lunch. The children will need to be arranged in the same way as the number chart, with each child holding a number card and each pair holding hands. Each appropriate pair jumps forward as 'two', 'four', 'eight' . . . are counted out aloud. With this set-up, the idea of even and odd numbers can be introduced. Even numbers are those with a pair; an odd number doesn't have a hand to hold.

Using numbers

Children need to understand the different ways we use numbers. Indeed, we sometimes find numbers in a context that was nothing to do with maths. Look at the following activity and decide which uses of the number '5' do not have mathematical relevance.

ACTIVITY

A 'number' table in the corner of the classroom gives an opportunity to show the wise range of uses of a particular number. Take the number '5'. The children could bring in: a plasticine birthday cake with five candles on it; a birthday card with a '5' for a five-year-old; a photo of someone's house with a '5' on the door; a calendar with the fifth of the month circled; a picture of a bus with a number '5' on it; a car with a '5' in the licence-plate number; a flower with five petals; a handprint with fingers numbered '1' to '5'; a shirt with five buttons; *The Very Hungry Caterpillar* (by Eric Carle) open at the five-fruits page; a clock set at five o'clock; a page from the *Yellow Pages* telephone directory with each '5' circled in the telephone numbers; a '5' on a barcode or postcode; a ruler with a '5'; or a 5p postage stamp.

Why count?

A group of children starting at primary school was asked whether they could count. Although they showed a wide range of counting ability, they all replied confidently that they could count. When asked why they counted, their responses were not quite what you might expect. They said they counted because they wanted to or because their teacher wanted them to. They also said they counted so that they could learn their numbers. Only a very small number of children actually suggested that they counted because they wanted to know how many things there were.

Children's slowness to grasp number-concepts has been attributed to an inability to see the point of it all. Children have to be given good reasons to count. That means finding every classroom opportunity for showing counting to be useful – for example while playing games you might include board games, carefully selected so that counting is an essential component.

Guessing

Encourage children to estimate numbers of things without counting. This is a valuable skill that enables children to develop an intuitive understanding of number as well as enhancing their mathematical confidence. Guessing the number of sweets in the jar is a very popular game and can be played with small numbers of sweets. However, as we all know, this is not as easy as it seems. To help children develop real skills in estimating it might be better to make up some suitable puzzles.

Concentrating on a counting game.

ACTIVITY

Use a pack of plain index cards. Decorate them with stickers or draw dots or stars on them. Ask the children to look at each card and guess how many there are. Then let them count and 'win' the card if they are right or nearly right (not more than one out). At first set up this up with no more than ten on a card and then extend to larger numbers. When showing them a card with over twenty, it is better for them to guess the range within which the card lies. For example, ask the questions: 'Do you think there are more than ten on this card?' 'Are there more than fifty?' 'Are there less than forty?' Make up mode cards with exactly twenty, thirty etc. dots on them. The child can then be asked to compare the two cards and decide, without counting, which has more and which less.

Writing numbers

Pre-school children often develop their own pictorial representation of counting. It is not uncommon for them to use simple tally marks or a series of blobs. Most will have been introduced to conventional numerals before entering school and will have sufficient co-ordination skills to produce recognisable numbers from 1 to 10. What is needed is lots of practice to familiarise them with number shapes.

Simple games, such as bingo, number lotto and number snap, help familiarise a child with numeral shapes. They can at first be played with specially made cards that only use the numbers 1 to 10. The games can then be extended to include the numbers 11 to 20 (or even higher). The basis of all these games is the matching of two identical number-shapes. They can be made more difficult by having one half of the matching pair as a number of dots. In snap, this would mean that 'snap' would be said when the number shape matched the card with the same number of dots.

Summary

- It is important for children to have a wide experience of the different ways numbers are employed. They need to be able to recognise when a number is being used as: a naming label (e.g. a 'number 6' bus); a means of putting things in order (e.g. a page number); or to represent the total of a set.
- In their first years at school children need to:
  - understand the significance of the size of a number and how it fits into the number system
  - be able to recite number names in the correct order
  - count sets of objects
  - count in tens and twos
  - estimate numbers
  - read and write numerals.

Calculations

> 'How can I tell if there are any children in my class who are ready to do sums?'

This must be one of the most common questions voiced by early years teachers. Yet this does not have to be a major issue. The ideas and language associated with adding and taking away sit very comfortably with basic counting activities. Suppose, for example, four toy cars are counted and two more are then found, it is natural to ask 'How many do we have now?' For children to do addition and subtraction sums it is essential for them to be able to count confidently both forwards and backwards.

There are several methods of teaching addition that rely on the use of specific apparatus. Before selecting one particular method it is important to recognise that young children develop their own strategies to perform the tasks of addition and subtraction. To clarify those used for addition, here are the responses of several children, about five years old, when asked to add 3 and 4.

- Jack counts four fingers on one hand and three on the other. He then counts them all starting at 'one'. This is known as **counting all**.
- Emma holds up four fingers and counts on three more, saying 'five, six, seven'. This is known as **counting on**.
- Jessica announces 'I know three and three are six so four and three must be one more. It's seven'. Here a **number fact** is being used. Double numbers are the most common number facts used by young children.
- Luke shows clear confidence in manipulating numbers. He explains that he added one to four to make five and then had two left. He then stated that five and two are seven. Asked how he knew that, he said 'I just know it'. Here's a child capable of developing his own strategy to solve the sum.

How to do sums

Counters, cubes, Cuisenaire rods, abacus, number lines and number ladders are all familiar classroom materials that help with calculating sums. Some schools show a strong preference for one particular method and use it extensively. Generally, most children can learn the same thing in a variety of different ways. It is probably best to use a wide range of activities to reinforce the essential concepts, noting which methods interest which child. If a child is not progressing, it can be helpful to try a totally different method. The most important thing is to avoid leaving the child with a sense of failure. Lack of success is most likely due to the child not having a deep enough experience talking about numbers or, more generally, exploiting the world of numbers. Earlier in this book there are many suggestions for promoting number confidence in younger children and these can be adapted and used with older children who are showing slow progress. Playing card games and mathematical board games with other children, and with adults, is an enjoyable way to practise and reinforce most of the early number skills.

Games reinforce strategy as well as counting.

Number facts

There is real value in teaching children some number facts. The ones they learn most quickly are usually those related to doubling, namely: three and three are six; four and four are eight; five and five are ten etc. These can be reinforced by holding up double dominoes and getting the children to call out the total (without counting). Probably the most important number facts which children can learn in their first years at school are the number bonds to ten.

ACTIVITY

A special pack of about thirty cards can facilitate the learning of number bonds. Take a stack of plain index cards and on each card write a number from 1 to 9. A game can be played with two children who have already begun to develop a good understanding of bonds to ten. They each have a pile of cards placed facedown and take it in turns to turn one over and put it on a central pile. If the card turned over adds up to ten with the card already lying on the top of the open pile, a child can win the whole pile by shouting 'ten'. The game continues until one child runs out of cards.

It is very helpful to point out the pattern in: nine add one is ten; eight add two is ten; seven add three is ten, etc. by using counters and showing clearly how one moves across from one number to its partner while the total remains the same. This can also be done very easily with the fingers of both hands.

Symbols

Once children begin to show an understanding of the processes of addition and subtraction, there is often a rush to introduce the appropriate symbols '+', '−', and '='. However, the introduction of symbols at this stage does not necessarily help the process of calculation and in some ways might hinder it. As explained at the beginning of this section, children develop their own useful strategies for solving sums. The examples given all involve several stages of computation and certainly can't be expressed as a simple '$a + b$' or '$a - b$' equation. It is much more important to develop number stories to illustrate how addition and subtraction work in real situations. Some children can quite easily learn number facts, such as seven add four is eleven, or the symbols that show that $7 + 4 = 11$. However they can be stumped if asked to solve the following problem: 'Ben was given 7p pocket money and his sister was given 4p more. How much did she get?'

Summary

- Children need to become familiar with the vocabulary associated with addition and subtraction, and understand real situations where these calculations are used
- There are different strategies used by children doing addition, namely:
    - counting all
    - counting on
    - using known number facts.
- Children need to know how to:
    - use different types of base-ten materials
    - count on from the larger group, when adding two groups of objects
    - use number bonds to ten for both addition and subtraction problems
    - count backwards for the purposes of subtraction.

Solving problems

At this level there are four topics to be covered: patterns; puzzles; predicting and estimating; sorting and matching. Each of these topics has been developed to suggest strategies for solving different types of problems. It is here that the process of analysis begins. The real challenge for solving any problem is to find a way to simplify it.

Patterns

Analysing and understanding patterns is fundamental to maths at every level. It is a skill that begins with young children recognising and working with patterns they find in the world around them. Patterns can be found in fabrics, wallpaper, carpets, plates, wall tiles, floor tiles, pavement slabs, brick walls, the arrangement of windows in a building, tiles on a roof, jewellery, petals of flowers, leaves on a twig, pine cones or zebra stripes. Patterns can be made using beads, printing, geometric shapes, Lego pieces, fruits, vegetables and tins of beans.

ACTIVITY

Very simple patterns can be created by alternating any two objects, shapes or colours. Take red and yellow Lego bricks and arrange them: red, yellow, red, yellow. Or use oranges and lemons in a similar pattern. Introduce more complex patterns to see if any of the children can continue it – try: red, red, yellow, red, red, yellow.... These can easily be done on worksheets but it is much more fun if the pattern is made with real objects, for example: tomato, tomato, potato. ... For children who enjoy this type of challenge the complexity can be increased by including a third category into the sequence as in: red, red, green, yellow, red, red, green, yellow. ... It often helps to clarify the pattern for a child if you chant it in a rhythmical way.

Patterns don't have to be made from objects; they can also be danced and sung. Musical instruments can be used to develop quite intricate patterns. The patterns can be drawn in pictures showing the order that instruments are played: big drum, little drum, triangle, big drum, little drum ... . As with all patterns, the children are challenged to say what comes next. It is worth experimenting with increasingly complex musical arrangements.

Puzzles

This topic is as wide as the imagination of the teacher and her pupils.

Standard suggestions include: exploring different ways of arranging five ladybirds on two leaves; distributing seven buttons in two boxes; or building a tower of bricks as tall as a cupboard. A good teacher will be prepared for some unusual answers to these fairly straightforward puzzles. Children have suggested that ladybirds can be stacked, arranged single or in groups, laid out upside-down, placed at one or other end of a leaf, or cut up and variously distributed between the two leaves! You could also have four ladybirds on one leaf and one on the other, or three ladybirds on one leaf and two on the other – these are the expected answers. It is obviously important for children to recognise the 'correct' answers so that they can give appropriate answers in tests. Teaching staff are in a good position to recognise that a child giving a more creative range of answers might very well be showing signs of higher ability. A teacher could explore how the language of the initial question needs to be modified in order to get only the required answer. For example, she could point out that if she had said 'whole ladybirds; then they couldn't be cut up.

Much of the puzzle work done in schools is based on looking at the number of ways various objects can be organised, rather like the ladybirds on the leaves. It might also be a good idea to introduce more unusual puzzles to promote lively discussion and lateral thought. The children could, for example, discuss ways of getting across the classroom without touching the floor. One bright child once suggested flooding the classroom and swimming across; another thought of using a helium balloon. These ideas generate lots of enthusiasm and analysis of ideas.

A good source of ideas can be puzzle books. Books such as *Snakes and Ladders* by Piers Harper and *The Great Two-Way Maze Book* by Juliet and Charles Snape are visually stimulating and engage two or three children in interesting problem-solving activities. Storybooks can also depict mathematical problems in an original and compelling way. Quentin Blake does this with humour in *Mrs Armitage on Wheels*. For bright children showing interest in big numbers, the lavishly illustrated *One Grain of Rice*, subtitled *A Mathematical Folktale*, by Demi, is irresistible. Also read *Weighing the Elephant* by Ting-xing Ye and Suzanne Langlois – a charming story set in China with a most unexpected solution to a difficult problem.

ACTIVITY

A popular puzzle is to provide groups of children with a bunch of super-long straws and sticky tape. Ask them to make the tallest structure they can within half an hour. For slightly older children, the challenge is made more difficult by stipulating that the structure must be able to support a marble on the top. This perhaps doesn't seem to have immediate maths content but, if you listen to the way the children discuss building the structure, the mathematical value of initiating this process of problem solving soon becomes clear.

Predictions and estimates

This subject has already been introduced in this chapter in the section on **'numbers and the number system'** and **'patterns'**. Estimating is an essential skill that helps a child gain confidence in handling numbers. It also helps them to spot when they have made a mistake. Making estimates can be extended to all types of measuring. Even before rulers and measuring jugs are being used accurately, children can be asked to guess how many steps it would take to cross the room, school hall or playground. They can guess the number of cups of water that will fill a bowl or the number of teaspoonfuls that fill a glass.

Sorting and matching

Most children have learnt simple sorting skills before they arrive in primary school. They can clear away their toys (with a little encouragement) and put them in the appropriate boxes. Once in school they get lots of experience of tidying up! However, to make sorting a more enjoyable and testing activity it is fun to make boxes containing a large mixture of items which the children have to sort out into a certain number of groups using their own criteria. This can link with work about materials in science or technology.

Measures, shape and space

Many teachers would call much of this section 'science' and not 'maths' but the distinction is largely irrelevant. Scientific investigations and activities provide the idea opportunity for developing an understanding of words like 'heavier', 'lighter', 'longer', 'shorter', 'more' or 'less'. Anything that can be measured simply should be measured. Length, weight, volume, time – they can all be introduced to the Reception class. It is not important at this stage to ensure accurate use of equipment such as rulers, weighting scales, measuring jugs; instead of absolute measurements, the real object is to introduce comparisons for example by encouraging children to decide who is the taller of two children and who has the longest feet in the class.

By using a simple two-pan balance, the weights of two objects can be easily compared. Similarly, by using a cup as a standard measure the volumes of two containers can be assessed. After a little experience children can be encouraged to judge the relative weights of two objects by hand and decide which is heavier before using the balance to check their decision.

Time

Children need a great deal of experience of 'time' before it can have any real meaning. We all know that time passes quickly when we are enjoying ourselves and ticks past very slowly when we are doing something boring. It is hard for a child to believe in a minute or an hour as a fixed length of time. This is made all the more difficult by adults telling children 'I'll be just a minute' and then spending much longer chatting with a friend! There are lots of good storybooks with time-related themes to help introduce the concepts of 'hours', 'days', and 'weeks'. Time also forms the basis of good, cross-curricular work, as can be seen in Chapter 6.

Children of this age begin by learning to tell the time using an **analog clock** (with hands). One helpful way to do this is to have twelve model clocks lined up. Adjust the first clock to show twelve o'clock and then put the others on each successive o'clock. The pattern is very clear and seen much more easily than if just one clock is used. It is also important to get a real geared clock to show how the hands move around as the time changes. In fact, every classroom ideally needs a working clock in a position where it can easily by seen by all. Nowadays many children's experience of measuring time comes from **digital clocks** (only with numbers, as on a video recorder), so it makes sense to do some of the classwork on time using both analog and digital clocks. Ideally, a digital clock would be placed alongside the analog clock.

Shape and space

Most of the everyday objects that children handle are three-dimensional and yet they usually arrive in primary school only knowing words for two-dimensional shapes, such as 'square' and 'circle'. Children need the vocabulary to describe both flat and solid shapes, and methods of analysis to distinguish between them. Most importantly, they need the experience of handling all sorts of shapes. There are special sets of regular geometric shapes and an enormous range of construction toys, including those using interlocking bricks, straws and marble runs.

Making patterns with geometric shapes.

ACTIVITY

There are many problem-solving games children can enjoy which are based on simple geometric understanding. Collect two categories of shapes (for example, all flat and all solid). Put each category into its own box and ask the children to find the rule for deciding which shape goes into which box. They can gradually progress to more difficult problems, such as distinguishing between straight-edged and curved shapes, or shapes with four sides and those with more. Another game promoting geometric analysis looks at what happens when a shape is rotated (this could be either a two- or three-dimensional shape); children often find this quite challenging when identical, irregular shapes made with Lego are displayed at different angles. This game can be modified so that the children have to spot the odd-one-out.

Observational skills are fundamental for the understanding of shape and space. Drawing simple structures helps children look carefully at what lies before them. Many teachers will seize every opportunity to help children develop descriptive language. A good game for stimulating children's observation and vocabulary involves placing a group of very similar objects (e.g. potatoes, stones) on a table. One child is asked to select an object without making it known to the other children. The child must then describe it well enough for the others to be able to identify it.

Summary

Children should be introduced to:
- the measurement of length, weight, volume and time
- related experiments
- two- and three-dimensional shapes and their names
- simple classification of shapes
- the way shapes change when their position is altered
- methods promoting careful observation
- the vocabulary associated with these topics.

There are many new mathematical ideas introduced in Reception and Year 1. It will take several years for most children to master much of this material. The important thing is that solid foundations are laid for future development.

6

Using Maths Across the Curriculum

Children need to encounter mathematical ideas and activities in a wide range of different contexts. In this way the concepts and language of maths are reinforced. Moreover, children begin to see the different ways in which the application of maths is relevant to the world we live in. Maths can be introduced as an integral part of many school or home projects. These cross-curricular links not only enhance the learning of maths, they also give extra interest to the project itself. Much of the contribution of maths to other subjects comes in the form of measuring both space and time. There are however, as we shall see, opportunities for highly creative applications of maths.

There are seven main headings in this chapter covering the following areas of primary school education: English; Science; Art, Design and Technology; Information Technology; History; Geography; Physical Education and Music.

English

The vocabulary of maths is found in our everyday use of language and in many of the storybooks that we read to children. Some stories can also be analysed to reveal the sequencing of events and word patterns. This can give children a clearer perception of these structures and helps with their understanding of the mathematical equivalents. There are many ways that work in literacy and numeracy can be made mutually supportive. The three examples below all use popular storybooks as a launchpad for developing activities with a maths angle:

1. *The Very Hungry Caterpillar* by Eric Carle has a repetitive structure with fruit to count, days of the week to order and the final metamorphosis of a caterpillar into a butterfly to observe. It is a structure worth analysing. A chart can be made to show what happens on each day of the week. The days of the week are listed down the side of the chart. Next to each day the appropriate number of fruit is drawn. The chart can be used as a simple counting game. The fruit pictures are covered over and the children encouraged to chant from memory: 'On Monday he ate ..., on

Tuesday he ate . . .' The children can be questioned about why the caterpillar eats progressively more and what is happening to him. It can be helpful for them to realise that the more he eats the bigger he gets, and the bigger he gets the more he eats – rather like children as they get older! A survey could be done to find out which fruit the children enjoy eating. The findings can be displayed on a simple bar graph and the class's favourite identified. This book can also lead to work on the symmetry of butterflies and then be widened to a general hunt for symmetry in nature. Using a mirror, the symmetry of the fruit in the book can also be investigated. Artwork can then be used to generate symmetrical patterns.

2. *Dear Greenpeace* by Simon James is about a little girl, Emily, who finds a blue whale in her garden pond. The book is in the form of correspondence between her and Greenpeace. Clearly this could stimulate all sorts of work on letter writing; it might also be rewritten as a series of telephone conversations. The maths interest here lies in the size of blue whales. They are over 30 metres long. A piece of string that length could be stretched out in the playground. Could it fit in Emily's pond? Make a paper circle the size of a garden pond and decide what could fit in it. How many goldfish? How many children standing next to each other? What about a seal or a giant water lily (it grows to about 2.5 metres across)? Try measuring other things with lengths of string, for example a car. Then cut lots of lengths of string, each as long as the car, and see how many of these are needed to equal the length of string measuring the blue whale. Try repeating this with string the same length as one of the children.

   There are many storybooks (see Appendix 1) that contrast very large and very small things. Books such as *Jim and the Beanstalk* by Raymond Briggs, *The BFG* by Roald Dahl and *The Teddy Robber* by Ian Beck can be used to create a topic on 'giants'. By looking at the illustrations it is possible to calculate the size of part of the giant and then draw it. For example, the child in the story might be the size of the giant's hand. Try to work out the size of his foot, eye, nose and then draw them. And what about his overall height – would his head go through the roof of the school? Full-size, cardboard models could be made of objects that appear in the stories, for example the spectacles, false teeth or coins in *Jim and the Beanstalk*. Make a giant plate with giant food out of card and papier maché. These props could create a really exciting 'giant' display in the classroom.

3. There are many books with food as an important theme. They include *Avocado Baby* and *The Shopping Basket*, both by John Burningham, and

Meg's Veg by Helen Nicoll and Jan Pienkowski. A classroom café can be set up using the food contents of one of these books. For the 'Avocado café' the children could concoct a menu of amazing avocado dishes, such as avocado burgers and avocado chips, which can all be made from green play-dough. The children may like to design menus, decide prices, and role-play waiters, waitresses and customers. If prices of each item on the menu are kept at the level of a few pennies, the children can be encouraged to calculate bill totals and make sure the customers give them the correct amount of money.

Summary

During literacy sessions teachers can support maths learning by choosing:

- stories with strong sequencing of events
- poems with clear patterns
- books with a content that includes counting, colour or measurement
- topics that can include mathematical activities.

Science

Almost every science-based project has a mathematical component. Many experiments involve some form of measurement or calculation. There is information to collect, organise, analyse and display. Here are three different categories of scientific activity; each utilises mathematical methods or ideas:

CLASSIFICATION

Any study of animals, plants or materials may look at how individuals can be grouped together. Animals can be classified into groups according to various criteria: what they look like (do they have fur, feathers or fins?); how they move (do they fly, swim, slither, walk?); or what they eat (do they eat grass, nectar, other animals?). This is an analytical process which has its mathematical counterpart in identifying sets and drawing logic diagrams.

OBSERVATION AND MEASUREMENT

Studying weather, for example, requires a whole range of measuring skills. A rain gauge can measure depth of water. Observation of the effects of wind can be given its equivalence on the Beaufort scale. Cloud cover can

Classifying mini-beasts.

be recorded as a drawing showing whether more or less than half the sky is covered. Temperature can be judged as cold, warm or hot and the position of the level of the alcohol in a thermometer marked. The children can then observe if the level goes up or down on successive days. Entering all these observations on simple charts can culminate at the end of the week in a class discussion on which was the wettest, coldest or windiest day.

EXPERIMENTS

There are many school experiments based on food. Try baking several batches of fairy cakes, each batch having a different ingredient missing. See if the children can predict what will happen to each set of cakes. The taste and texture can be described afterwards.

Summary

Maths is an integral part of many science activities. Children need to learn:

- simple methods of measurement and recording data
- ways of displaying data
- the value of predicting experimental outcomes.

Taking measurements during the solar eclipse at a children's science summer school.

Art, design and technology

Measurement is often an integral part of art, design and technology. Model making also requires an understanding of the use of scale (see the 'giant' example in the section 'English' earlier in this chapter).

A C T I V I T Y

A topic based on buildings can use photographs to look at patterns in the arrangement of bricks, windows and roof tiles. Model buildings can be made from a whole range of different materials: clay, Plasticine, Lego or wooden lollypop sticks. Little people, made to scale, can get through doorways. A doll's house could be constructed using boxes as rooms and appropriately sized furniture made from card. The decoration of each room can be themed according to a particular pattern – a dotty bedroom would have spots on the wallpaper (which could be specially printed), spotty fabric for curtains and bedcovering; a stripy living-room could be designed in a similar way.

Once you start looking you will find patterns and symmetry in an enormous number of manufactured items. Curtain and dress fabrics, wallpapers and carpets are obvious sources of patterns. Look also at towels, tea towels, tablecloths, crockery, wall tiles, ornaments, furniture, frying pans – you will find patterns and symmetry everywhere.

Information technology

Most children starting school will already have encountered computers, usually by playing games on them. There are many maths computer programmes to support work in the classroom, should you choose to use them. It is helpful for children to understand the wide range of things that a computer can do – keep information as words or pictures in its memory, do calculations very quickly or control a robot or spaceship.

A C T I V I T Y

A project about symbols can utilise the icons on a computer. The children could look out for symbols in their everyday life, such as the signs for: no smoking; women's and men's toilets; children crossing a road; speed limits; or changing the volume on a television remote control. They could design their own signs for use around the school: don't run in the corridor; don't shout in class; don't draw on the walls; no dogs in the playground; smile and be happy. The discussion may be expanded to include numerals such as 1, 2, 3 ... and '+', '−', '=' signs. It can be a real surprise for children to recognise that these are all different types of symbol.

Concept keyboards

These are becoming commonly used in primary schools. They are very useful for younger children because they don't rely on reading or writing skills. They consist of paper overlays that fit onto a keyboard. The overlays have squares faintly outlined on them but you can draw on larger cells. There is special software for programming the computer so that it responds when different parts of the keyboard are touched. The overlays can be used with pictures, symbols or words. It is important not to jam pack the overlay with too much information. The list below gives some general ideas but it is easy to adapt them to any topic:

- **Simple matching**. Pairs of pictures can be drawn or cut-outs stuck on.
- **Sequencing using**: numbers; simple pictures that tell a story (such as a child getting out of bed, getting dressed); pictures that represent a familiar story; natural events (such as seasons, growth of a seed, egg-to-frog cycle); or historical developments (such as transport, homes, clothes – illustrated with pictures showing examples at different times during history).
- **Matching words and pictures**. Words such as 'full', 'empty', 'tall' and 'short' can be matched with suitable pictures.
- **Counting**. The numeral needs to be matched with a drawing showing the correct number of objects.
- **Ordering**. Make a large picture of clearly identifiable people in a running race. On the overlay put individual pictures of the people. Under each picture can be written the appropriate ordinal ('first', 'second', 'third' …). The pictures have to be entered in the same order as they appear in the race picture.

Summary

- Model making promotes an understanding of scale.
- Manufactured products can be selected to illustrate patterns and symmetry.
- Computer icons can be part of a wider understanding of symbols.
- Concept keyboards have a wide range of maths applications.

History

Children need a clear understanding of the passage of time before they can grasp historical ideas. The subject of time is one that can be revisited throughout primary school. Timelines can be introduced in the first school years, each child making their own personal timeline showing when they were born and marking on it other important events (when they began to walk, the birth of a sibling, going on a special holiday or starting school). This is a way of visualising a child's own history. The timeline can easily be extended backwards to include the birth and major life events of other family members. Other recent events can also be given their place on the timeline. Find out what dates the children would like to add, for example when: the first man walked on the moon; CDs were invented; their favourite storybook was written; the money we have was first used; videos were invented; or salt and vinegar crisps first went on sale. The timeline can grow backwards as children's experience of history is enriched through the teaching of different periods. The whole school can contribute to a timeline so that it stretches all the way along corridors and includes the periods different classes are working on.

There are many children's books with time themes which help a child grasp the way time is measured. Try *The Stopwatch* by David Lloyd and Penny Dale, and *Tick-Tock* by Eileen Browne and David Parkins. Other books, such as *The Tiny Seed* by Eric Carle and *Seasons* by John Burningham, show the wider picture of the cycle of seasons through the year. A child of five or six years of age is only just beginning to identify the shape of a year. They can probably only clearly remember the last year or two of their lives, so the pattern of months and seasons will not yet have been fully recognised.

Time is a topic that reaches very naturally across many subject areas. Its measurement is important in science and maths. Time underlies the whole structure of history and it also belongs in the domain of geography. You can't explain day and night without introducing a child to a rotating world globe. How can children understand changing seasons, here and in other parts of the world, without having a notion of what planet Earth looks like? Once some of these ideas are in place, some of the class may be ready to consider whether it is morning everywhere in the world at the same time. *Out there somewhere it's time to . . .* by Mick Manning and Brita Granstrom is a challenging book that explains how the time of day depends on where you are in the world. To get a good overview of the longer passage of time reach for *Tick-Tock* by James Dunbar in the *Wonderwise* series.

ACTIVITY

While young children find concepts such as centuries and decades almost meaningless they can develop a sense of the sequence of events.

If a topic such as buildings is examined in a historical context, children will often be able to put in correct chronological order pictures of a reconstructed Anglo-Saxon hut, a medieval castle, a black-and-white timbered Tudor house, a red-brick Victorian house and a modern concrete building. This can also be done with different forms of transport (horse, raft, bicycle, steamship, steam train, car, aeroplane, rocket). Clothes can also be used (Roman toga, simple Anglo-Saxon clothes, Elizabethan dress, Victorian clothes, modern fashion). Books such as the *Yesterday and Today* series, published by Watts, look at social history over the last hundred years in a way that Key Stage 1 children are able to appreciate.

You can find lots of other great ideas for enriching visits to historical sites in *Teacher's Guide to Maths and the Historic Environment* (by Tim Copeland) from English Heritage. There are also some interesting posters from Tarquin Publications which illustrate the mathematical content of historical themes. They not only decorate the classroom walls in an imaginative way but also act as a springboard for related topic work.

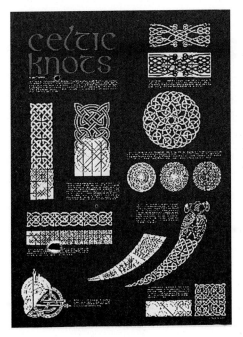 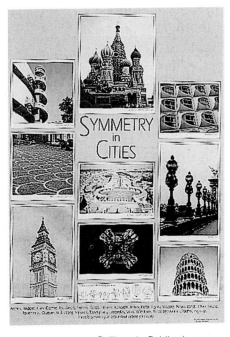

Posters can highlight mathematical links with history, art and geography. © Tarquin Publications, 1999.

Children love playing with money. Ask each child to bring in ten pennies. Show them where the date is on the coin. Make a coin chart with each date clearly written on it and little circles drawn underneath for sticking pennies on with double-sided tape. The children then have to sort out where their pennies should be stuck. The teacher can point to a particular date and ask: 'Does anyone have these numbers on a penny?'

Geography

In the first years of school this subject is usually centred on the school itself and its immediate locality. Plans can be drawn of the playground or rooms in the school. To produce a detailed plan of the playground, make a list of all the things the children can see as they walk around the playground. Then allocate an object for each child to draw: a climbing-frame, part of a building, rubbish bin, tree, flowerbed or bench. The teacher can then mount a large plan of the playground on the classroom wall. The children cut out their drawings which can be stuck on the plan in the appropriate place. Plans of rooms can be made in a similar way.

An early project in Reception could involve reading *Rosie's Walk* by Pat Hutchins and making a large wall-map to show a long winding path. Ask the children to tell you the places visited in the story and then list them. Encourage the children to work in pairs and illustrate a particular place. The illustrations are then cut out and stuck on the wall-map in the correct order. A potato can then be cut in the shape of a hen's footprint and used to show the path the hen took. Finally, the children are invited to tell the story of what happened at each location.

A large wall-map depicting the neighbourhood of the school can be used for children to show where they live. If the map is also produced in A4 size, a photocopy can be given to each child. Those children whose homes are on the map can mark the route they take on their way to school.

Drawing treasure-maps is lots of fun. They can be 'aged' by smearing a little dirt on them and tearing the edges to make them look jagged and worn. The children can draw an island and indicate various features, such as a river, bridge, lake, trees and huts. Symbols could be used to represent these. The map could then be constructed in three dimensions with papier-mâché to create hills. Don't forget to include a treasure chest or an 'X' to mark the spot where it's buried!

Summary

- In history personal timelines and time topics help children develop a historical understanding of time.
- Children can be introduced to historical sequences in the development of buildings, transport or clothes through the ages.
- In geography plans based on stories can be constructed and maps and plans of the school neighbourhood can be used creatively.
- Treasure maps can be converted into three-dimensional models.

Physical education and music

All babies show an immediate appreciation of rhythm. Physically this can be expressed as gentle rocking or vigorous bouncing. We are also tuned in from birth to the rhythmic sound of song and music. These are pleasures that stay with us throughout our lives. At school, P.E. and music are often favourite lessons when children feel they can relax and express themselves with a sense of freedom and individuality. It is an opportunity to encourage children to experience the patterns of rhythm physically by jumping, skipping, hopping or clapping.

ACTIVITY

Music lessons in which instruments are used offer lots of opportunity for maths-related activities. Rhythmic patterns can be tapped or shaken on percussion instruments. They can be represented on a chart by symbols for quiet and loud sounds or for short and long ones. Quiet sounds might be shown in pale blue; loud sounds could be shown in red. Short lines can represent a brief tap, and longer lines a sustained hit. An arrangement where different instruments play in a particular sequence can also be shown on a chart with symbols. Each instrument is given a simple shape – this is best done with shapes that correspond to some aspect of the geometry of the instrument: a xylophone might be depicted as a rectangle, a drum as a circle, maracas by a circle on a stick and a triangle as a triangle! The successful result will be for the sequence 'circle, circle, triangle, circle, circle ...' to produce 'bang, bang, tinkle, bang, bang ...'.

Singing sessions can easily be themed to include songs with particular relevance to a topic in another part of the curriculum. A project on animals might include the songs: *Old Macdonald had a Farm*, *Five Little Ducks*, *The Animals Went in Two by Two*. All these have, of course, intrinsic mathematical value.

Sport

Competitive sports soon introduce children to words such as 'first', 'second', and 'last'! Many games require keeping score and a scoreboard will certainly help children to read and write numerals. The introduction of a stopwatch can bring extra interest to any running or jumping race. End-of-year sports' day sometimes has the school divided into several large groups with points being awarded to the winning groups: three points if someone comes first, two points for the second, one for third. It is a good idea to spend some time explaining to younger children how the scoring system works and then to make up score sheets so that they can keep a record as points are won. Perhaps they would like to check the grand total at the end.

In the playground

Use your outdoors climbing frame to investigate geometric patterns and, with spray cans of playground marking paint, make hopscotch outlines and number snakes. If there is chalk available for the children, they will be able to draw out their own playground games.

Summary

Children can accumulate mathematical experiences while:

- performing physical exercise routines to music
- playing musical instruments
- 'reading' symbolic music
- using a stopwatch to time races
- keeping score during games.

7

Developing Maths and Support Outside School

It is important to remember that the reason most of us needed to learn maths was because it provided us with a collection of tools to use in our everyday lives. We learned it for practical reasons. The maths that happens in the classroom is, most of the time, one step removed from that in the real world: children play at shopping, work out problems on paper, experiment with ways of measuring things or count using a number line. Of course, making space to learn how maths works is important and good teachers will constantly link their teaching to real-life situations. The main reason most young children learn maths is so that, when they are older, they can work out, for example, whether they are given the correct change in a shop, how to use bus and train timetables, or how much petrol they will need for a long car journey.

Teachers can try very hard to show children the reasons for learning maths, but turning the classroom into the mathematically rich world outside will never be possible. This is why it is so important that families and out-of-school carers, including those in after-school and holiday clubs, take a positive interest in children's learning of mathematics and help to share with them the many ways in which it is used in the wider world.

It is probably impossible for any of us to get through a day, in this part of the world at least, without using any of the mathematical ideas that are learnt by younger children. Few of us go through a day without telling the time, for example. The challenge is to support parents and carers, and teachers too, in realising that all adults can help children with maths. Many parents and carers do not recognise how much help they already give their children.

One mother described helping her five-year-old daughter get Christmas cards ready for her home-group at nursery.

The mum had a list of the names of the children in the group and they'd chosen a box of cards that contained four different designs. She sat with her daughter while the girl sorted them out into piles of identical cards. The child counted out five of each sort. Then she decided which card would be best for which friend, carefully matching the pictures to something about each child: 'Jenny likes "Twinkle, twinkle little star" so she'd like this one'. They filled in the cards together and at the end they counted them – there were nine for the children in the group.

'So how many envelopes will we need?'
'Nine.'

They matched the cards and envelopes, addressed and sealed them. Then they counted the cards left over. There were eleven.

'How many must there have been in the box when we started then?'
'Eleven here and nine we've written'

Then they worked out how to add that up using both their sets of fingers. They concluded it was twenty and looked on the box lid. The child recognised the number '20'. Their answer was right.

'Hang on a minute, there's ten children in your group, not nine.'
'Oh no! How many cards have we got again?'

The child recounted the cards, then suddenly she realised that she was the missing person. She plus the nine other children in the group made ten altogether.

The mathematical content of this session related to real things that were important to the child. It also included, for good measure, some reading, writing, creative thought and discussion. A Reception class teacher would be pleased with this quantity and quality of work from one child in a lesson but of course it needed one-to-one support and no primary class teacher could give that quantity of time to just one child. Parents' and carers' ability to give extended one-to-one time is unique. The family in our example were just sorting out a few Christmas cards – sending cards for festivals or special events is something that most of us do.

Most adults do everyday maths mentally. Children never see us adding up the shopping in an approximate way as we go round the supermarket or working out whether there's enough space left on a video to record a television programme. Maths is taken for granted by many of us, and its real-life applications become invisible to children. We need to make the maths we do visible in an informal way.

More ideas

Here is a selection of activities that are easy to do out of school with younger children. Some of them are only ever possible outside the classroom setting.

Going for a walk

Identify house or flat numbers. They may be continuous, odd on one side of the road and even on the other. Are you counting forwards or backwards as you walk down the street? There may be a number missing, what was it? Why? Was a house knocked down?

'What's your favourite number? OK. Let's find all the number sevens.' If you start looking for numbers in an urban setting, or in the home, you will see them everywhere.

Use the phone

How does the phone book work? What are dialling codes? Let children dial numbers for real calls to real people. Talk about 999 calls and emergencies. (The phone system uses strings of numbers as labels, like bus numbers. These numbers are not to do with counting.)

Cook and eat together

Try magazines, adults' and children's cookbooks or ask other teaching staff and parents for ideas for things to make. Sweets, biscuits, cakes and puddings are usually very popular. Children can help with the family's main course meals as well. Choosing, peeling and chopping vegetables involves counting and discussing shapes and sizes. Baking uses measuring: spoonfuls, cupfuls and weighing, as well as cutting out or forming different shapes. Using the oven means setting temperatures and watching the clock so that nothing burns. Doubling or halving quantities according to the numbers of people to be fed gives good practice in manipulating ideas linked to the two-times table. If you have access to balance scales, let the children play with them and use metric weights if possible: only grams and kilograms tend to be taught in school nowadays. Estimate, then look at, the weights given on packages. Try one, two or three kilograms to start with, then maybe half-kilogram packs. Bags of flour or sugar usually come in these sorts of sizes.

Design platefuls of food that have been laid out in patterns, or make cakes and biscuits decorated with repeating patterns. Sharing out food equally – cutting pizzas, cakes or sandwiches into equal parts – practises simple division and fractions. Fruit presents lots of mathematical opportunities: try guessing the number of segments and pips in your satsuma before you peel and eat it. How close was your guess? Sort the cherries into singles, pairs and triples. How many pairs are there and how many cherries all together? Let children state how many fish fingers or potatoes they want for their supper and count them onto the plate together. Some children like to guess the number of chips or peas they are served, then count the food accurately as they eat it.

Money

Parents could consider giving children pocket money. If possible, make sure a good selection of coins is available on pocket money day and let children work out which ones they will take that week. Finding your pocket-money in small change is very exciting when you are six years old, even if you can only manage to count it out in one pence pieces. Handling real money, especially larger denominations, is an unusual event in a classroom – it would be hard to supervise. It's much easier at home with your purse or wallet. Children who are given the opportunity to manage their own money at home seem to get the hang of how it works very quickly. In fact, many of the children we have encountered who are supposed to be struggling with maths are amazingly adept when it comes to calculating their own savings and planned purchases.

Exchanging a £1 coin for 100 pennies generates a new toy that can be used for playing shops at home, counting, sorting into piles of ten or making into patterns. Help children to pay cash for small items in the shops too. If they can manage money sums easily, ask them to work out the change from the £1 coin they've given to the shopkeeper or ask them to help you work out how much two loaves of bread would cost when you know the price of one.

Moving house and packing

Moving house, or packing goods for storage, involves working with the real-life equivalent of a three-dimensional jigsaw. Even young children can

Taping the centre, corners and edges of packing boxes.

help with taping up the boxes to pack things in – there will be plenty of conversations about centres, edges and corners and whether the tape is long enough or guessing whether all the things to be taken will fit in the van.

Packing presents and parcels uses skills in deciding whether the paper will fit around the gift without leaving gaps or how long to make a piece of sticky tape.

DIY and gardening

DIY projects at home require research and planning, costing and buying materials, counting, measuring, doing the building work or repairs and evaluating how well you have done it afterwards. You can see or use the results. Talk to the children about what you are doing, share the process and let them do all the maths within their capabilities even if it is only holding the tape-measure or helping you guess if a shelf will fit a gap before you measure it. Buying carpet or other flooring may involve drawing a map of a room to scale. A trip round the kitchen flooring section of a superstore may lead to discussions about the different kinds of tiling patterns printed on the vinyl.

Gardening uses similar thinking and planning skills. If anyone you know has a vegetable garden or allotment, see whether the children could help to map the layout for the coming season and help them work out the number of seeds that must be bought given the length of rows. Some people manage to grow quantities of vegetables in growbags on balconies so access to land need not be a problem. Many rural communities still have village-based produce competitions at the end of the summer and trying to grow the longest runner bean or the heaviest marrow is great fun. Sunflowers are traditionally grown for competitions too. Plant the 'giant' varieties; they usually grow at a very fast rate and can be measured regularly.

Maximum/minimum garden thermometers can be interesting to read, especially in the autumn when days may be quite warm and nights frosty. Remember to use Celsius measurements.

Travelling and holidays

There is plenty of maths involved in holiday activities: working out distances travelled and costs of tickets, looking at traffic signs and road markings, visiting tourist site and museums and thinking about dates in history, counting sand castles and sorting the shells and pebbles collected at the beach, and guessing how hot the temperature was that day. Involvement in swimming or other sports activities will no doubt include talk of distances or the numerical scores in competitions. Zoos and aquariums will enable you to discuss sizes, shapes and patterns, make comparisons and count.

Comparing the tropical fish in the tank.

Unexpected maths opportunities may happen when you are out and about. This family invented a new unit of measurement when they stopped for a quick look at a tourist site.

'The children had seen pictures of Stonehenge on the television and we decided to stop off there when we were on a long distance car journey. We hadn't got much time so we couldn't walk round the stones but just looked at them from a distance. It was hard to get a sense of how big they were so we looked at the people standing near the stones. There was a man who looked really tall in comparison with the other people there. We worked out that it would have taken about three of him standing on top of each other to be as tall as the upright stones. The children decided that the biggest person they knew was Graham, their uncle. They said "the stones are three Grahams big – that's *enormous!*". We now use 'Grahams' as our way of measuring things that are huge.'

Collecting

Some children like to collect anything. Toddler passions for pebbles and shells may progress to free toys from cereal packets and then on to the more traditional collections of coins, stamps, rocks and minerals or fossils. Collections are important. Much can be learned about quantity, comparisons, sorting and ordering and, maybe later, displaying, recording, researching and financially valuing. Encourage collecting. Even if you are hard pressed for space, many collections will take up very little room and the mathematical benefits are great.

Clocks, timers and alarms

When a child starts to become aware of clocks you can ask them to go and check the time for you. (Send them to read times on the hour to begin with.) It can get more complicated as they get the hang of it. Help them set an alarm clock to wake you up in the morning. Use a kitchen timer to time activities – tidying up is often a good one: 'Can we get everything put away in five minutes?' Then race the timer and get a sense of what can be achieved in the time available.

Model making

It costs nothing to collect and recycle packaging materials for children to make models with. Keep a cardboard box topped up with empty cereal packets, kitchen roll tubes, old wrapping paper, boxes from supermarkets, chocolate boxes, the inner cardboard cones from machine-knitting wool, egg boxes, coffee jar lids, washed drinking straws and so on. Add some safe scissors, felt tip pens, sticky tape and PVA glue. You then have a kit to which any child can turn for creating and constructing models: castles, vehicles, doll's houses, space ships? Designing and making models uses lots of three-dimensional thinking, fitting and measuring.

Toys and games

Many games that children enjoy playing out of school use logical thinking, strategic planning and mathematical ideas. Games of all kinds often fall into these categories: the more modern ones and traditional games, such as ludo, draughts, battleships, dominoes and chess. Card games, even 'snap' which demands skill in matching at speed and solo 'patience' games where you build sequences of numbers, have a mathematical content.

Many manufactured construction toys are very useful to support children's spatial learning. It is very helpful to have construction toys for playing with. These include traditional wooden bricks, plastic bricks such as Lego, Duplo or Sticklebricks and train sets where the tracks and train-engine combinations can be assembled by the child.

Toys in the bath are important. Much of children's early learning about volume of fluids comes from play with water. Save empty shampoo bottles of different sizes. Add a bought plastic funnel and maybe a set of plastic

Designing and building detailed pirate ships from Lego.

measuring cups and children will play happily with these, making all kinds of mathematical connections.

Children's pictures

Don't forget to take a closer look at children's pictures, particularly ones they have drawn based on their own ideas. They can show you the changes in their mathematical understanding. The pictures shown here were both drawn by four-year-olds. If you ignore the different styles, you will notice that each person and dog has been drawn with accurate numbers and arrangements of facial features and limbs. Both the children could observe, count and record their observations accurately. Significant learning has already taken place. Drawings can be the key to lots of thinking and understanding. Ask children about their pictures.

Television Programmes

You might want to record some of the children's educational television programmes about maths. BBC2 and Channel 4 produce yearly catalogues (see Appendix 3). Even if the children have seen them in school they might enjoy watching them again, maybe over the holidays.

The above suggestions are only a small beginning. There are many resources available that give ideas to parents, carers and out-of-school childcare workers on how to help children with maths. For more details see Appendix 1.

Children's pictures of a person with a dog show careful observation and counting.

Summary

- Most of us learn maths for practical reasons, for everyday use as a tool in the world outside school.
- Many parents and carers do not realise how much help they already give their children. Their ability to give extended one-to-one time is special.
- Parents and carers can make the maths of everyday life visible, by talking about it and encouraging children to participate in it, at home and in the wider world.

Communication

Home–school links need to be strong and parents and teachers need to know what each other is doing if children are to be well supported in their mathematical learning.

At a **whole school** level, the staff may take the initiative by holding sessions for groups of parents who want to understand more about the teaching of maths and for parents to contribute ideas of what might be possible at home. Some schools keep a maths notice board in the hallway which contains information about maths projects, ideas for things to do at home, book reviews and posters about where adults can go to further their own skills in maths. Schools may consider running a weekly maths surgery where parents can go, for example, to talk about how best to help their children.

At a **class** level, the staff may give talks and facilitate meetings with parents of new Reception class children to discuss all aspects of school life, including beginning maths at school. It can be really helpful if classes or year groups have some means of letting parents know what is happening in all areas of the curriculum each week. Again, some schools use notice boards outside the classrooms. Many send home newsletters. Homework is often supposed to be done at home in conjunction with a parent or carer's support. It is important that sufficient instructions are included because some ways of doing or thinking about maths have changed since parents or carers were at school.

The home–school diary system, frequently used for communication about reading, can be extended and used for parents and staff to communicate **one-**

to-one about individual children's learning in other areas of the curriculum. It can be helpful for parents to have a means of letting staff know about difficulties sooner rather than later, for example, when a child has found homework too difficult or didn't get on with the supply teacher so didn't understand any of the previous week's maths – it happens! Parents need to know how to book a session to discuss particular worries with a class teacher, before a child switches off from maths completely. Termly parent–teacher evenings may not be sufficient to deal with potential problems.

Using parents' skills

It can be enormously helpful in the classroom to use the mass of skills that parents, grandparents and carers have.

Many adults have professional backgrounds or hobbies that could help demonstrate maths in action. If a class is looking at right angles, is there a plumber amongst the parents who could demonstrate bending pipes into right angles and explain different kinds of plumbing joints? The school's pipe work could be inspected for interesting angles. Is there a carpenter who could show how to use his or her equipment to cut wood square or make interesting right-angled joints and help the children glue their own simple ones? Is there an architect who could show plans and architectural models of buildings? Is there a picture framer, a builder, a carpet fitter or a graphic artist who could help? Many parents are only too glad to give an hour or so to talk about a subject in which they have expertise. This is one way to bring the outside world of real-life maths into the classroom. Specific requests for help often have positive responses where general ones fail.

Parents who are confident in helping with maths in the classroom can be invaluable, especially during work with small groups in 'the daily maths lesson'. It is important that they are given clear information about the role they are expected to take. Parents may also be willing to help make maths games for the classroom or for a school maths games library which all families can use. Many maths games are simple to make and can be made more durable by laminating them in plastic covers or covering them with clear, sticky-backed plastic. Some schools, working with parents, have created some wonderful libraries of resources.

Coping with testing of children

The first SATs test that children sit in state primary schools are in Maths and English and take place towards the end of Key Stage 1 when the children are about seven years old. There is a wide range of opinion about their usefulness or necessity. However, they are a statutory requirement. Many schools do not tell young children they are being tested – events will be conducted in a way that do not feel like a traditional 'test', and parents may not know the exact details of days or times.

Despite attempts to play down SATs at Key Stage 1, some children know exactly what is happening, some parents get extra coaching for their children or do extra work and practise papers with them at home so that they 'do better'. Schools obviously want good results but there is a danger that things may get too pressured for some children and there may be a case for teaching staff and parents to have an open dialogue about how to manage the statutory tests without children feeling stressed.

Summary

- Home–school links need to be strong if parents and staff are to know what each other is doing and if children are to be well supported in their mathematical learning.
- It can be helpful to use the skills that parents already have, both as classroom volunteers and professionally.

8

Moving on with Maths

Throughout this book we have acknowledged the wide range of maths language and experience that we can all easily contribute to the mathematical development of children. As they move on through their primary school, mathematical education begins to assume a more formal structure. It can be a real challenge for teaching staff to maintain children's enthusiasm for maths. This might be achieved through the introduction of cross-curricular projects and innovative problem solving activities. These can place considerable strain on the timetable and the teacher, however, and this chapter opens with some ideas on how to structure the teaching of maths so that there is more time for a whole range of maths-related activities.

Those of us who have custody of the education of children carry the responsibility of providing pupils with the foundations of the essential maths knowledge and skills they will need throughout their adult lives. Some children in our care will become engineers, surveyors, architects, bank managers (and maths teachers!) – for them maths will become an integral part of their working lives. However, for all children, maths will be an essential, everyday life skill. They will need to be able to: check a bank statement; read an electricity meter; follow a recipe; calculate the materials needed for DIY; assess the quality of statistical 'facts' cited by politicians; recognise the real costs of loans and overdrafts; compare different saving schemes; and understand how to budget effectively.

Whether you are a parent, childminder, early years teacher or classroom helper you can help children along the path of *their* mathematical journey through life. In this chapter we take a broad overview of the main topics covered in primary school maths. We look back at how mathematical development began in earliest childhood and was nurtured through pre-school years. We then look at progress through primary school and the way it prepares the child for subsequent maths work.

The ongoing challenge

> Alex and Jan, two seven-year-olds, were engrossed in a mathematical board game during a maths class. The game was designed to practise addition and subtraction skills.
> *Teacher*: Are you enjoying that maths game?
> *Alex*: This isn't maths!

This pupil's response focuses our attention on one of the main problems confronting anyone who teaches maths – how do you teach the subject so that children regard it as fun and see its relevance to non-formal maths work?

For some children at primary school, their maths education might contrast with that at nursery. This is, to some extent, inevitable. Nursery is play-centred, while school is a more disciplined and structured environment. As children move through primary school the mathematical ideas become more abstract, with the result that some children may begin to perceive maths as an isolated subject with little relevance to their wider experience of the world. The difficulties that children encounter at this stage can be damaging to their future progress in the subject. It can be useful to introduce special activities in the form of puzzles, problems and cross-curricular topics. These can help children appreciate maths as an enjoyable subject with relevance to many real-life situations.

For those involved in classroom teaching, the suggestion of introducing extra maths project work poses a dilemma. Having spent the session allotted to maths making sure that we cover the whole syllabus, can we still justify devoting time for extra maths in project work?

We all readily recognise that nowadays the demands on teaching staff are considerable, in terms of both time and energy. There are not only the requirements of the Numeracy Strategy, which are detailed and extensive but there are also the mounting pressures for SATs results to meet the expectations of pupils and parents. Unfairly, the reputation of a school and its teachers may be damaged by a poor set of results.

Stretching the timetable

There can be ways to 'stretch' the timetable. To begin with, the amount of time spent on any one particular topic can be looked at in more detail. Some schools rely more heavily on worksheets or workbooks that give copious practice in a particular skill. There are children who obviously enjoy the process of filling pages of sums. They find the repetitive nature of doing lots of simple work very undemanding. However, the amount of practice a child needs in a topic is probably a lot less than that allocated in the workbook. There can be a sense in which the book takes over. Teaching staff can use their professional judgement to decide when a pupil is ready to move on and, even if it is felt that more practice is needed, it can be introduced in a different context: maybe as part of a problem-solving project.

An increasingly widespread practice in teaching maths is to hold pupils back until they get everything right. When children complete a worksheet, getting a couple of sums wrong will sometimes delay their progress onto more advanced work. Again, those who are teaching the child can use their own judgement to decide that a few mistakes don't necessarily mean that more, virtually identical, worksheets need to be completed. A brief discussion with the child should reveal whether or not the child understands the work.

Homework provides the opportunity to do lots of exciting maths outside school. It generates interest if the homework has only an oblique connection with the current syllabus work in school. It is a chance for children to undertake time-consuming investigations into patterns or numbers, for example, without the need for classroom supervision.

Summary

Maths interest can be maintained by:
- approaching a maths topic in a variety of ways including discussion and games
- increasing the pace of learning to match the ability of the individual child using differentiated activities
- giving challenging homework.

Curriculum maths

This section covers some of the main maths topics that are introduced during Year 2. These form main mathematical themes throughout primary school and beyond. The learning of maths is a continuous journey. Each section reflects some of the earliest mathematical experiences of very young children. We look at the progress of maths through pre-school and primary years.

Numbers and counting

The naming of numbers and the beginning of counting began quite naturally when we played with a baby's little toes and chanted the rhyme about each 'little piggy'. Right through nursery age we sang rhymes to reinforce the sequence of numbers. Parallel to this were all the opportunities we found to count everyday objects. Whether in nursery school or at home, the young child is hearing numbers and associated mathematical vocabulary many times, every day of its life. This constant repetition begins to implant the understanding that numbers have fixed order.

A pre-school child finds the world full of new experiences and begins to adopt an ever-extending vocabulary to describe them. As co-ordination skills develop, the opportunities for exploring the physical world bring new opportunities for mathematically related activities such as sorting, matching, sequencing, building and measuring.

Using play to explore counting and symmetry in the Reception class.

By the time children enter the Reception class at school, some of them will already be able to say the numbers from one to ten very reliably in the correct order. Some will understand that the final number we reach when counting is the total number of things in the whole group. They will begin to add two groups of things together, a process that they might first have met as a toddler. Having counted two objects, a carer might 'discover' another object and say 'here is another one, and that makes three'. Similarly, perception of subtraction has its earliest roots in things *taken* away from little children.

As children move through Year 1 their familiarity with numbers allows them to learn number facts which help in simple calculations. Doubles such as two and two are four, five and five are ten . . . have a rhythm which children soon learn. They will also apply their writing and reading skills to number words and numerals. Their growing understanding of numbers will enable them to grasp the significance of place value.

More calculations

During Year 2, work begins on fractions. Many of us will have begun this years earlier with toddlers – for instance, at teatime we cut their bread 'in half' or even into 'four quarters' and persuaded them to eat 'a half a slice' more. In school we now extend this idea to small groups of things, for example: 'take six sweets and give half of them to a friend'; here we are also on the threshold of division. Words such as 'sharing' have long been part of the adult vocabulary addressed to small children. Suddenly the word has a new meaning. Small children, told to share a toy, have to learn that this means one child plays with it for a short while and then passes it on to another child. It doesn't mean 'cut it in half'. Children may well have already met the idea of sharing a group of things in which case there will be some understanding to build on.

Through the years of Key Stage 2 children will move on to perform multiplication and division using two-digit and three-digit numbers. Children need a strong sense of place value and a good understanding of what is really being calculated during these mathematical processes. In secondary school these calculations will be performed with decimals and fractions. If the children don't understand the underlying principles, they won't be able to solve more complex problems and will find the extension of these procedures to algebra extremely difficult.

Summary

- The language and ideas of maths continue to be extended with the introduction of fractions, multiplication and division.
- It is essential that children don't rote-learn calculation skills but develop a clear understanding of underlying principles.

Shape and space

The baby who lies in its cot and tries to focus on a mobile wafting above is making a first venture into the surrounding three-dimensional world. Handling and exploring objects will soon bring a greater understanding. The young child explores shape further using construction toys or doing junk modelling. These kinds of activities may enhance spatial awareness later on.

At primary school, children are introduced to a whole range of two- and three-dimensional shapes. Lots of boxes and tins from the supermarket give an interesting variety of forms to analyse into different groups. Look out for packs in the shape of prisms, pyramids and cones, and collect ice-cream containers that are truncated cones (i.e. cones with the top, pointed part sliced off). It's fun to cut them open and lay them flat, so that the children can realise that they all started out as flat pieces of card. Can the children bring to school a shape that can't be made from a flat piece of card? Cut open an old ball to demonstrate the problem. This can be linked to the difficulties faced by mapmakers who drew flat maps of our spherical planet.

Summary

- Early experience of using construction toys helps provide the foundation for future understanding of geometrical problems.
- Playing with two- and three-dimensional objects provides children with a growing understanding of space and shape.

Solving problems

This is the heart of maths. There are two main aspects to this area of education:

- You can carefully select problems so that children get the chance to apply the methods of calculation they have learnt. This is where those methods can be practised without inflicting on children too many similar, repetitive sums. Look for some challenging problems to replace standard sums.

- Puzzles and problems make children *think*. (See Appendix 1 for books that will be useful for this.) Why not start a chess group? Children around the age of six or seven can learn the basic moves very quickly. If you don't know how to play, get someone in from the local chess club to teach the children; these clubs often have someone who specialises in working with juniors. Don't forget to learn with them! Chess problems are brilliant mind-benders. The chess club will be able to provide some simple problems; try others in *Usborne's Chess Puzzles*.

For more able children, you'll find great value some of the problems in books for older children: *The Amazing Mathematical Amusement Arcade* by Brian Bolt and *The Amazing Science Amusement Arcade* are full of interesting ideas; *Who Tells the Truth?* by Adam Case has demanding logical puzzles which can be used with able children even as young as seven years old.

Working with a friend on a chess problem.

The beauty of a pattern in the first snow of winter.

Children who discover the joys of problem solving are probably the ones who will want to continue with maths and science at a higher level. The great problem solvers of the past hundred years showed amazing leaps of imagination. Einstein is probably the best known (we referred, in Chapter

4, to the unusual nature of his mind already evident when he was a child). It is fascinating to discover the childhood experience of another great twentieth-century physicist, Richard Feynman. He is not well known to the general public, but in the world of science he is one of the giants. He won the Nobel Prize for Physics in 1965 and was probably the most outstanding theoretical physicist in the second half of the twentieth century. He always insisted that he owed his mathematical genius to his first maths teacher, his father. The account Richard Feynman has left us of the early learning experiences he shared with his father is an inspiration to anyone who looks after or teaches young children. When Feynman was very young, his father brought home a set of little tiles in different colours and arranged them in simple sequences: two white, a blue, two white. The young boy had to find the next tile. His mother complained that it wasn't fair to expect so much of such a little boy but his father explained 'I want to show him what patterns are like and how interesting they are. It's a kind of elementary mathematics.'

Feynman's father was not educated in maths or science but he seemed to understand intuitively how to teach his son. We know that he also read to his young son from the *Encyclopaedia Britannica*. He never tried fill his head with facts but used information to stimulate the boy's interest and imagination. When reading about Tyrannosaurus Rex the article stated that 'this dinosaur is twenty-five feet high and its head is six feet across'. Feynman's father explained 'that would mean if he stood in our front yard, he would be tall enough to put his head through our window up here. But his head would be too wide to fit in the window.' Long after Richard Feynman had become a world famous scientist, he recalled how much he owed to those first lessons and the impact they had on him for the rest of his life. He said 'I've been caught, so to speak – like someone who was given something wonderful when he was a child and he's looking for it again. I'm always looking, like a child, for the wonders I know I'm going to find.' Through his quest for those wonders he was able to give the scientists of today original insights into quantum theory, gravity and nuclear physics – some of the most challenging areas of modern physics.

Summary

- Try using problem solving to develop mathematical thinking.
- Very young children can be given simple pattern problems.
- Children as young as six years old can learn chess and solve related problems.
- More able children can be given problems from books for older children.

Those of us who spend much of our lives teaching young children – whether we are parents, childminders, nannies or teaching staff in a nursery or primary school – are faced with an immense challenge. We must provide these young minds with the maths they need to develop essential life skills. We must also have the imagination to feed their minds with the joy and beauty of mathematics. Perhaps many of us will discover for the first time in our lives just how easy maths is and how much fun it can be. An accomplished university mathematician we know attributed her love of the subject to the teaching ability of her first primary school teacher who had this motto: 'Make numbers your friend and you will have a friend forever.'

Glossary

base ten

When we count we use units 0 to 9 and then we write 10, which shows one ten and no units. This is using a base-ten number system. Base-ten materials include number lines, number squares, Cuisenaire rods – any piece of equipment that helps to demonstrate the structure and use of our number system.

cardinal number

The numbers 1, 2, 3 . . . used for counting are called cardinal numbers. When a set of objects is counted the last number gives the **cardinal value** of the set.

conservation of number

If you have a set of objects the total number doesn't alter no matter how you arrange the objects. This is called conservation of number. It seems very obvious to us but young children believe that when a set of objects is moved around the total number of objects changes: for example, if the objects are spread over a larger area the young child will think their number has increased.

counting

When children are able to count there are basically four things that they must be able to do:

- use the correct number word for each object counted
- count each object only once
- stop counting when each object has been counted
- understand that the last number they count gives the cardinal value of the set.

They should also understand that

- the cardinal value of the set remains the same irrespective of the order of counting
- the number word is not a name for the object, so that when counting is finished the words are not labels that remain attached to the objects.

counting all

When two sets of objects are added together the total is found by counting all the objects present starting with 1, 2 . . .

counting on
This is a method of adding two numbers or two sets of things together. The first set contains a known number of objects, previously counted. When more are added the total count begins with the cardinal value of the first set. For example when two objects are added to a set of six, the count goes '6, 7, 8'.

estimation
With practice children can learn how to make simple estimates of the approximate number in a set or the quantity in a bottle. Accurate estimation requires a great deal of experience in careful counting and measuring.

nominal numbers
Numbers that are used to give a name to something are called nominal numbers. Examples of nominal numbers include: the number of a bus; telephone numbers; numbers on car registration plates; credit card numbers.

number bonds
To facilitate addition it is useful for children to learn the pairs of numbers that add to ten, such as: 2 and 8; 3 and 7. These pairs are known as number bonds.

number line
A diagrammatic representation showing the correct order of numbers is known as a number line. It can show negative as well as positive numbers.

number square
The numbers 1 to 100 are arranged in rows of ten numbers. The columns are lined up so that the pattern of our base-ten number system can be clearly seen. In this number square all numbers ending in 1 (such as 1, 11, 21, 31) are lined up under each other.

ordering
This is a way of arranging objects or numbers so that they are laid out in increasing size or quantity.

ordinal numbers
These numbers show an order when counting. First, second, third ... are ordinal numbers.

patterns
These are arrangements of objects or numbers that follow a regular rule. They are a collection of repeating sequences.

place value
This is the position of a digit in a number. The digit will have a different value depending where it appears in a number. For example, the number 333 has the digit three meaning three hundred, three tens or three units depending on its place.

sequence
A sequence is a row or line of numbers, drawings or objects, which follow a rule. It forms a linear, or line pattern.

tallying
This is a system of counting using marks to represent the number of objects counted. The marks are usually short, vertical lines – one is drawn as each item is counted. (Tallying is used in cricket matches to keep count of the number of runs scored.)

two-dimensional shapes
These shapes have length and width but no thickness. Triangles, squares, rectangles and circles are some of the first two-dimensional shapes that children learn.

three-dimensional shapes
Solid shapes with length, width and depth are three-dimensional. Spheres, cubes, cuboids, cylinders and cones are some of the first three-dimensional shapes that children encounter.

symmetry
There are two different kinds of symmetry:

1. *Rotational symmetry*. A shape can be rotated into more than one position and still look the same. The letter I has rotational symmetry because it looks the same if you turn it through 180° so that it is upside down.

2. *Reflection symmetry*. A picture, or shape, with reflection symmetry can be folded along a line so that one half looks like a reflection of the other half. If you place a mirror along this line of symmetry, the reflection will look like the same as the other half. This is the reason it sometimes called *mirror symmetry*.

Appendix 1

Some ideas for books to use with children

New books are being published all the time. The following are details of books mentioned in the text and others that are our favourites. They have been divided under five main headings:

- Counting
- Measurement
- Colour and shape
- Observational skills and problem solving
- General

Although books are listed under only one subheading, their content could justify them appearing in other categories. Many of those listed show sequencing and other verbal patterns and so a separate group has not been made for them.

Counting

My Oxford 123 Number Rhyme Book, Oxford University Press, 1994
Quentin Blake – *Cockatoos*, Red Fox, 1994
                 – *Mister Magnolia*, Red Fox, 1999
Valerie Bloom – *Fruits: A Caribbean Counting Poem*, Macmillan, 1997
John Burningham – *The Shopping Basket*, Picture Lions, 1995
Eric Carle – *The Very Hungry Caterpillar*, Penguin, 1997
Kathryn Cave and Chris Riddell – *Out for the Count*, Frances Lincoln, 1991
Faustin Charles – *A Caribbean Counting Book*, Barefoot, 1996
Penny Dale – *Ten in the Bed*, Walker, 1990
John Foster and Carol Thompson – *Counting Rhymes*, Oxford University Press, 1998
Christopher Gunson – *Over on the Farm*, Picture Corgi, 1996
Mick Inkpen – *One Bear at Bedtime*, Hodder, 1989
Inga Moore – *Six Dinner Sid*, Macdonald, 1991
Martin Waddell and Patrick Benson – *Owl Babies*, Walker, 1994

Measurement

Pamela Allen – *Mr Archimedes' Bath*, Picture Puffin, 1990
Ian Beck – *The Teddy Robber*, Picture Corgi, 1989

A. H. Benjamin – *A Duck So Small*, Magi, 1998
Raymond Briggs – *Jim and the Beanstalk*, Picture Puffin, 1996
Eileen Browne and David Parkins – *Tick-Tock*, Walker, 1996
John Burningham – *Seasons*, Red Fox, 1993
Eric Carle – *The Bad-Tempered Ladybird*, Puffin, 1977
   – *The Tiny Seed*, Puffin, 1997
Trish Cooke – *When I grow bigger*, Walker, 1994
Roald Dahl – *The BFG*, Puffin, 1989
James Dunbar – *Tick-Tock*, Watts, 1998
Jane Hissey – *Jolly Tall*, Red Fox, 1993
Pat Hutchins – *Titch*, Red Fox, 1997
Simon James – *Dear Greenpeace*, Walker, 1991
David Lloyd and Penny Dale – *The Stopwatch*, Walker, 1986
Mick Manning and Brita Granstrom – *Out there somewhere it's time to . . .*,
   Watts, 1999
Henry Pluckrose – *Readabout: Measurement*, Watts, 1997
   – *Readabout: Time and Clocks*, Watts, 1997
Alf Proysen – *Mrs Pepperpot*, Young Puffin, 1996
Martin Waddell and Barbara Firth – *Can't you sleep little bear*, Walker, 1998
Robert E. Wells – *Is a Blue Whale the Biggest Thing There is?* Watts, 1995

Shape and colour

Dayle Ann Dodds – *The Shape of Things*, Walker, 1996
John Hindley and Margaret Chamberlain – *The Wheeling and Whirling-Around Book*, Walker, 1994
Shirley Hughes – *The Nursery Collection*, Walker, 1996
Mick Inkpen – *The Blue Balloon*, Hodder, 1989
David McKee – *Elmer*, Red Fox, 1991
Korky Paul and Valerie Thomas – *Winnie the Witch*, Oxford University Press, 1998
Henry Pluckrose – *Readabout: Wheels*, Watts, 1997

Observational skills and problem solving

The Amazing Science Amusement Arcade, Cambridge University Press, 1984
Quentin Blake – *Mrs Armitage on Wheels*, Red Fox, 1996
Brian Bolt – *The Amazing Mathematical Amusement Arcade*, Cambridge University Press, 1994
Adam Case – *Who Tells The Truth?* Tarquin, 1996
Demi – *One Grain of Rice*, Scholastic, 1997
Martin Handford – *Where's Wally*, Walker, 1996

Piers Harper – *Snakes and Ladders*, Walker, 1997
Mick Manning and Brita Granstrom – *What's Under the Bed?*, Watts, 1997
– *What's Up?*, Watts, 1999
Jean Marzollo and Walter Wick – *I Spy Mystery: A Book of Picture Riddles*, Scholastic, 1993
Michelin – *I-Spy* books
David Norwood – *Chess Puzzles*, Usborne, 1991
Juliet and Charles Snape – *The Great Two-Way Maze Book*, Julia MacRae, 1995
– *The Giant Book of Scary Mazes*, Julia MacRae, 1998
– *Electric Mazes*, Julia MacRae, 1999
Ting-xing Ye and Suzanne Langlois – *Weighing the Elephant*, Annick Press, 1998

General books

Maths Together, Yellow Set Age 3+, Walker, 1999
Maths Together, Green Set Age 5+, Walker, 1999
Janet and Allan Ahlberg – *The Baby's Catalogue*, Puffin, 1998
Quentin Blake – *Simpkin*, Red Fox, 1995
John Burningham – *Avocado Baby*, Red Fox, 1994
David and Wendy Clemson – *My First Maths Book*, Dorling Kindersley, 1996
Sarah Garland – *Doing the Garden*, Puffin, 1996
– *Doing the Washing*, Puffin 1995
– *Going Shopping*, Puffin, 1995
Jane Hissey – *Old Bear*, Red Fox 1991
Pat Hutchins – *Rosie's Walk*, Puffin, 1970
Helen Nicoll and Jan Pienkowski – *Meg's Veg*, Mammoth, 1997
Helen Oxenbury – *Dressing*, Walker, 1981
Michael Rosen and Helen Oxenbury – *We're Going on a Bear Hunt*, Walker, 1993
Elfrida Vipont – *The Elephant and the Bad Baby*, Puffin, 1999

Useful resources for adults

The list doesn't attempt to be comprehensive. We have just brought together some useful books that are currently available. Keep an eye open for the exciting, new resources that are being published all the time.

Ron Adams – *Primary Colours 1: Teaching in Colour*, Stanley Thornes, 1998
– *Primary Colours 6: Supertopics*, Stanley Thornes, 1998
Ruth Aplin – *Assisting Numeracy: A Handbook for Classroom Assistants*, Beam, 1998

Sue Atkinson – *Developing Numeracy Skills*, Hopscotch, 1999

Kathie Barrs – *Music Works*, Belair, 1999

Wendy and David Clemson – *Primary Colours 3: Maths in Colour*, Stanley Thornes, 1998

– *Learning Targets for Numeracy*, Stanley Thornes, 1999

Tim Copeland – *A Teacher's Guide to Maths and the Historic Environment*, English Heritage, 1991

Ray Gibson – *You and Your Child: Number Games*, Usborne, 1993

Neil Griffiths – *Primary Colours 7: A Corner to Learn*, Stanley Thornes, 1998

Anne Henderson – *Maths for the Dyslexic*, David Fulton, 1998

Barbara Hume and Kathie Barrs – *Maths on Display*, Belair, 1998

Frances James and Ann Kerr – *Creative Computing*, Belair, 1997

Elizabeth Matterson (ed.) – *This Little Puffin*, Puffin, 1990

Ann Montague-Smith – *Mathematics in Nursery Education*, David Fulton, 1998

Linda Pound – *Supporting Mathematical Development in the Early Years*, Open University Press, 1999

Ian Thompson (ed.) – *Teaching and Learning Early Number*, Open University Press, 1999

Angela Walsh (ed.) – *Help Your Child with Maths*, BBC Books, 1988

Number at Key Stage I, BEAM, 1995

Learning Mathematics in the Nursery: Desirable Approaches, BEAM, 1997

Starting from Mathematical Ideas: Big Numbers, BEAM, 1997

Number in the Nursery and Reception: A framework for supporting and assessing number learning, BEAM, 1998

Assisting Numeracy, BEAM, 1999

What do we mean by maths? Pre-school Learning Alliance, 1997

Maths through play, Pre-school Learning Alliance, 1991

Count and figure it out together, Basic Skills Agency available from Admail 524, London WC1A 1BR, tel: 0870 600 2400

Early Learning Goals, QCA, DfEE, 1999

The National Numeracy Strategy, DfEE, 1999

Photocopiable resources

Blueprints, Stanley Thornes, 1999

Mathematical Masterfile KS1, Domino Books, 1999

Platform Maths 1 and 2, Leopard Learning, 1998

Main series of maths textbooks and workbooks

Some of the better known schemes are:

- *National Curriculum Ginn Mathematics*, Ginn
- *New Abacus*, Ginn
- *Maths 2000*, Nelson
- *Nelson Mathematics*, Nelson
- *SPMG*, Heinemann
- *Heinemann Mathematics*, Heinemann
- *New Heinemann Maths*, Heinemann
- *Longman Primary Maths*, Longman
- *Oxford Maths Zone*, Oxford University Press
- *Cambridge Primary Mathematics*, Cambridge University Press

Appendix 2

The Baseline Assessment

All state-maintained primary schools have a legal requirement to assess all new four- to five-year-old pupils within seven weeks of them starting school.

Class teachers have overall responsibility for the assessment of individual children, although they may delegate some of the work to other teachers or assistants. The assessment takes place in one-to-one situations, by observing each child as part of a group and by using existing knowledge of the child's typical performance in school.

Tests used are accredited by the Qualifications and Curriculum Authority (QCA).

The testing on maths ability includes assessing whether a child can:

- sort sets of objects according to specified criteria
- count objects up to ten
- solve addition and subtraction problems with totals up to ten
- explain an addition sum
- recognise and write numbers 1–10

The National Numeracy Strategy

In March 1999 the Department for Education and Employment (DfEE) published the *Framework for teaching mathematics from Reception to Year 6*. It forms part of the training materials that support the National Numeracy Strategy. As part of this strategy all state primary schools in England were required in September 1999 to provide a structured daily maths lesson from 45 minutes to one hour. This has become known as the 'Numeracy Hour'. The *Framework* is not statutory and schools can adopt a different structure but they will have to demonstrate that they are covering the same contents and achieving results which are at, or above, the expected level given in the National Numeracy Strategy. Schools with special needs may also be exempted in a similar way. Schools taking this route are advised to do so in close consultation with their Local Education Authority.

It is compulsory to teach the maths syllabus which is laid out in the National

Curriculum Order. The *Framework* is a detailed guide which supplements the National Curriculum. It includes a set of yearly teaching programmes with recommendations for the number of days to be spent on each topic. There is also a substantial section where detailed examples are given of what a child should be able to achieve mathematically by the end of each school year.

Following the *Framework*'s recommendations, a typical maths lesson at Key Stage 1 will be divided into three basic components:

- 5–10 minutes of whole-class mental maths practice
- 30–40 minutes for the main teaching input where the class can be taught as a whole, in groups or in pairs. If teaching is done in groups or pairs then the whole class should be working on related activities
- 10–15 minutes is spent rounding off the lesson. This is done with the whole class and is designed to provide time to help children assess their own progress. It is also during this session that the way maths relates to other subjects is discussed.

Private nursery, preparatory and other schools teaching primary-aged children, as well as parents who are home-educating their children, are not subject to the National Curriculum or the guidelines generated by the National Numeracy Strategy. However, all schools and home-educating families registered with their Local Education Authority are subject to inspection and are still expected to meet certain educational requirements.

Early Learning Goals

Early Learning Goals (applicable from September 2000) is an advisory document produced by the QCA for the DfEE. It provides information on the learning goals, principles and aims for children at the foundation stage, which includes children from the age of three to the end of Reception year. It replaces the earlier *Desirable Learning Outcomes*. It does not specify a curriculum but gives recommendations of what it expects most children to be able to achieve by the end of the foundation stage. These learning goals are in line with the key objectives in the National Numeracy Strategy and are consistent with the requirements of the Baseline Assessment.

This is the status, at time of publication, of government recommendations. They are constantly being modified so it is very important to ensure that you are familiar with current practice. Details can be obtained from the QCA or DfEE (see Appendix 3).

Appendix 3

Other resources

Publishers

Publisher's catalogues

These are usually free and can be ordered direct from the publisher – a library should be able to help you find addresses and phone numbers. Alternatively look in the *Writer and Artists Year Book* (published by A & C Black) for details of all magazines and book publishers in the UK, and some other countries.

BEAM
Maze Workshops
72A Southgate Rd
London N1 3JT
Tel. 020 7684 3323

DIME Projects
18 Hillfoots Road
Stirling FK9 5LF
(available from Tarquin Publications)

Tarquin Publications
Stradbroke
Diss
Norfolk IP21 5JP
Tel. 01379 384 218
These catalogues will thrill anyone working with children. They are filled with really creative maths books and related resources. They are also the distributors of DIME teaching materials.

Walker Books
87 Vauxhall Walk
London SE11 5HJ
Tel. 020 7793 0909
They produce an early years book list relating to the Numeracy Strategy.

Media

To find out details about educational programmes and related resources contact:

BBC Information
PO Box 1116
Belfast BT2 7AJ
Tel. 0800 100 222

Channel 4 Schools
PO Box 100
Warwick CV34 6TZ
Tel. 01926 436444

Organisations and other useful sources of information

The Mathematical Association
259 London Road
Leicester LE2 3BE
Tel. 0116 221 0013
http://www.m–a.org.uk/
An association of teachers and students of elementary mathematics. It runs conferences and local activities and produces journals: *Primary Mathematics* and *Mathematics in School* (both for teachers) and *Symmetry Plus* (for young mathematicians – a useful resource for able children).

The Association of Teachers of Mathematics
7 Shaftsbury St
Derby DE23 8YB
Tel. 01332–346599
http://www.atm.org.uk
Provides support and information to teachers and local groups. Co-ordinates an Early Years Working Group and an annual conference and produces journals and other publications.

NRICH Online Mathematics Club
http://www.nrich.maths.org.uk/
Website run through Cambridge University for children, teachers and parents. A good source of mathematical enrichment activities, including discussions, online magazines, puzzles, games and a question/answer facility for all ages and levels including teachers.

The Education Library Service
Nottinghamshire County Council Leisure Services
Glaisdale Parkway
Nottingham NG8 4GP
Produce two very helpful thematic fiction lists (titles indexed by theme, e.g. animals, seasons, family, journeys) in book form.

Pre-School Learning Alliance
69 Kings Cross Road
London WC1X 9LL
Tel. 020 7833 0991
Sell their own publications. Contact them for a catalogue.

English Heritage
Education Service
23 Savile Row
London W1X 1AB
Tel. 020 7973 3000
Sells resources and videos.

The Letterbox Library
Unit 2D
Leroy House
436 Essex Road
London N1 3QP
Tel. 020 7226 1633
This book club is particularly useful for multicultural books, including those with a mathematical content.

Cambridge Learning
Burwash Manor Farm
New Road, Barton
Cambridge CB3 7BH
Tel. 01223 262777
Software suppliers with useful catalogue. They allow you to try before you buy in their shop, or you can purchase through mail order.

Binary Arts
Distributed in the UK by Ravensburger
Bessemer Close
Bicester OX6 0JD
Tel. 01869 363800
Produce strategy and logic games, and also 3-D puzzles.

Maths Year 2000
57–58 Russell Square
London WC1B 4HP
A year of mathematical events and related publications.

Information about special needs

Anything Lefthanded
5 Charles Street
Worcester WR1 2AQ
Tel. 01905 25798
Shop selling lefthanded resources and training videos.

The Basic Skills Agency
Commonwealth House
1–19 New Oxford Street
London WC1A 1NU
Tel. 0800 700987
Help with adult numeracy.

The British Dyslexia Association (BDA)
98 London Road
Reading RG1 5AU
Helpline: 01189 6682711
Admin: 01189 662677

The Dyslexia Institute
133 Gresham Road
Staines TW18 2AJ
Tel. 01784 463851

National Association for Gifted Children
Elder House
Milton Keynes MK9 1LR
Tel. 01908 673677

National Association for Able Children in Education
Westminster College
Oxford OX2 9AT
Tel. 01865 245657

National Deaf Children's Society
15 Dufferin Street
London EC1Y 8UR
Tel. 020 7250 0123

Royal National Institute for the Blind
Education Support Services
RNIB Information Service
224 Great Portland Street
London W1N 6AA
Tel. 020 7388 1266

Magazines

Child Education, Nursery Projects, Infant Projects and others from **Scholastic Magazines**:
Scholastic Ltd
Freepost CV 3065
Westfield Road
Southam
Warwickshire CV33 0BR
Tel. 01926 816250
Magazines for early years professionals and teachers which contain general articles and ideas for teaching numeracy and cross-curricular project work.

Government resources

The National Numeracy Strategy Framework for teaching mathematics from Reception to Year 6 (and other DfEE publications) available from:

DfEE Publications
PO Box 5050
Sudbury
Suffolk CO10 6ZQ
Tel. 0845 60022260

The Department for Education and Employment, London
Tel. 020 7925 5000

The Qualifications and Curriculum Authority (QCA)
QCA Publications
PO Box 99
Sudbury
Suffolk CO10 6SN
Tel. 01787 884444
The QCA produces information about the National Curriculum, the Key
Stages, statutory tests, information for under-fives professionals including
the Baseline Assessment, and a variety of reports.

Index

able children 58–65
addition and subtraction 16–17, 50,
    57, 87–90, 109–11, 123, 126
art 101–2
    see also drawing
Avocado Baby 98–9

babies and toddlers 1–18
    bath time 5
    beginning mobility 13–17
    confident walking 17–18
    conversations 2, 4–5
    developmental sequences 1
    dressing 5–6, 20
    exploration of physical
        environment 6, 13–14
    feeding 11
    learning spectrum 19
    new born babies 1–4
Basic Skills Agency 76
The BFG 98
board games 41–2
books 23, 46, 49, 50, 60, 76–7,
    97–9
    for able children 64
    for babies and toddlers 11–12
    for dyslexic children 68
    puzzle books 92, 128
    reading with children 25–7
    shape, colour and pattern themes
        46
    time theme 104

cardinal numbers 49, 132
charts, see graphs
chess problems 128
classifying and grouping 18, 24–5,
    40, 99
clocks 94, 116

clothes
    and colour 28
    dressing 5–6, 20
co-ordination 62–5
collecting 24, 60, 116
colour 27–8, 42–6, 72
computers 71, 72, 102–3
concept keyboards 103
conservation of number 50, 132
cooking 32, 37–8, 111–12
correspondence of numbers 5
counting 16–17, 25, 29–33, 39,
    50–2, 111, 118, 125–6, 132
    when dressing 5–6
    when feeding 11
    and fingers 23, 82
    from one to ten 79–82
    when playing 8–9
    reasons for 34, 57, 85, 109–10,
        112
    to more than ten 83
    in twos 84
        see also numbers
counting all 88, 132
counting on 88, 133
curriculum 36–8, 56, 79, 124–31

Dear Greenpeace 98
design 101–2
diaries 119–20
disabilities see learning disabilities
displays 57, 97–8, 105, 106–7
division see multiplication and
        division
DIY projects 114
dominoes 42
drawing 52–3, 64, 75, 118
dressing 5–6, 20
dyscalcula 68–9

dyslexia 66–8
dyspraxia 69–70

Einstein, Albert 69, 129–30
estimation 33, 50–1, 60–2, 85–6,
    93, 133

Feynman, Richard 130
food 11, 32, 37–8, 111–12

games *see* play; toys and games
gardening 32–3, 114
geography 106–7
graphs 53, 98, 101
guesswork *see* estimation

hearing impairment 71
history 103–4
holiday activities 114–16
home–school diaries 119–20
homework 119, 124
housework 31–2
    see also tidying up

illustrations in books 27
information technology 102–3

jigsaws 22, 42
Jim and the Beanstalk 98
junk modelling *see* model making

kitchens 13–14, 37
    see also model making

language 24–9, 97–9
    conversations with babies 7
    first words of babies 16–17,
        17–18
    talking to babies 2, 4–5
    see also maths vocabulary
learning disabilities 65–74

dyscalcula 68–9
dyslexia 66–8
dyspraxia 69–70
hearing impairment 71
visual impairment 71–2
left-handedness 70–1

matching 34, 39–40, 87, 93, 103
maths
    at school 78–97, 119–121,
        122–130
    challenges 56–77
    cross curricula 97–108
    early skills 19–35
    pre-school skills 36–55
    vocabulary 18, 26, 38–9, 48,
        74–5, 83, 97
mealtimes 32, 112
measurement 53–5, 93–6, 99–101
Meg's Veg 98–9
mobiles 4
mobility 13–17, 21
model making 43, 64–5, 102,
    116–17
money 48–9, 99, 112
multiplication and division 12, 126
music 10–11, 107–8

National Numeracy Strategy 78–9
nominal numbers 49, 133
number bonds, 82, 133
number facts 87–90, 126
    concept 28, 85
    large numbers 59–62, 83
    reading 51–2
    recognition 27, 111
    recording 52–3
    using 49–50, 59, 84
    writing 52–3, 61–2, 86–7
    see also counting
nursery 36–55

nursery rhymes 10–11, 46, 49

ordering 41, 103, 133
ordinal numbers 11, 49, 133
outdoor play 19–21, 37–8, 44–6, 54, 69, 73–4

packing 112–14
parents 9, 36, 41–2, 56, 75–7, 109–21, 130–1
patterns 7, 42–7, 59, 64, 91, 102, 112, 114, 133
physical education 107–8
place value, 61, 134
play 7–9, 42–6
   physical activities 7–9
   role-play 34–5, 47–8
   sandpits 73–4
   structured play 22
   tea parties 34
   water play 9–10, 73–4
   see also toys
playgroups 36–7
pocket money 112
problem solving 59, 91–3, 95, 127–30
puzzles see toys and games

reading 25–9, 51–2
   see also books
rhymes and songs 3, 10–11, 46, 50
role models 75
role-play 34–5, 47–8

sandpits 73–4
SATS tests 120–1
scaffolding 22
science 93–6, 99–101
sequences 6–7, 26, 41, 67, 97–8, 103, 104, 107, 134
shapes 3–4, 15, 22, 37–8, 42–6, 64–5, 94–6, 127, 134

The Shopping Basket 98–9
songs 30, 46, 108
   see also rhymes and songs
sorting 24–5, 33, 40–1, 93
spatial skills 3–4, 10, 62–5, 94–6, 127 and dyslexia 67
symbols 27, 51, 52, 90, 102–3, 107
symmetry 45, 64, 98, 102, 134

tallying 53, 134
technology 101–3
television programmes 118
temperature 100–1, 114
testing children 120–1
tidying up 13–14, 31–2
time 46–7, 94, 116
   history 103–4
timelines 104
toddlers see babies and toddlers
toys and games 14, 15–16, 41–2, 63–5, 87, 117–18, 120
   bricks 44–5
   jigsaws 22, 42
   mobiles 4
   money 48–9
   puzzles 41–2, 64, 91–2, 123, 128
train sets 46
   see also play
travelling 114–115

The Very Hungry Caterpillar 97–8
visual impairment 71–2

water play 9–10, 73–4, 117
weighing 54, 94
woodwork 43
words 74–5, 97
writing numbers 52–3, 61–2, 67, 68–9, 86–7